The Beginner's Observing Guide

An Introduction to the Night Sky
for the Novice Stargazer

Leo Enright
The Royal Astronomical Society of Canada

An Invitation to Membership in
The Royal Astronomical Society of Canada

The Royal Astronomical Society of Canada is the oldest and largest association of astronomers in Canada. Its history goes back to the middle of the nineteenth century. The Society was incorporated in 1890 and received its Royal Charter in 1903. Its membership includes professional astronomers, but it is largely an amateur organization with members of all ages, from all walks of life, and also from many countries around the world. In Canada there are 22 branches or "Centres of the Society" in the major cities across the country. Current membership is more than 3000. The common bond among the members is an interest in and a desire to promote the study of astronomy and the related sciences.

Serious users of this observing guide would benefit from membership in the Society. Members receive the publications of the Society and are entitled to other benefits. Information about joining may be obtained from the secretary of the nearest Centre or from the National Office of the Society. More information about the Society, including the addresses of all of the 22 Centres and the National Office, is given in Chapter 19 of this book (pages 124 - 135).

The cover photograph of the Full Moon is by the author.

Canadian Cataloguing in Publication Data

The National Library of Canada has catalogued this publication as follows:

Main entry under title:

The Beginner's observing guide

Enright, Leo, 1943–
"An introduction to the night sky for the novice stargazer".
ISSN 1188-1798
ISBN 0-9695804-1-X (1993)

1. Astronomy – Observers' manuals. I. Royal Astronomical Society of Canada. II. Enright, Leo.

QB63.B42   520   C92-031664-6

Acknowledgements

The idea of producing a beginner's observing guide for use by novice stargazers began over ten years ago. For several years, the idea was discussed by a number of dedicated members of The Royal Astronomical Society of Canada who eventually were part of a group that was called "The Mini-Handbook Committee". At the meeting of the Society's National Council in July, 1990, I was asked to assume the editorship of the project, and eventually the book which preceded this one, *The Beginner's Observing Guide 1992*, made its appearance. I want to thank the members of the original committee, particularly Dr. John Percy, who supported the concept for many years.

The star maps which are a very important part of this book are adapted from those designed and drafted by Dr. Roy L. Bishop of Acadia University and are copyright material of his and of The Royal Astronomical Society of Canada. Dr. Bishop also provided some of the material for the chapter on astronomy badge requirements in the Scouting movement.

A special acknowledgement is due to Mr. David Levy who contributed to Chapters 8 and 14. David's enthusiasm for observing the night sky has been rewarded with the discovery of eighteen comets (at last count) which bear his name.

Contributions of material and ideas were made by Mr. Pat Kelly, Mr. Michael Watson, and Mr. Randy Attwood. Suggestions too numerous to mention, received from Society members from coast to coast, have been incorporated. My wife, Denise, Past-President of the Kingston Centre, has provided support and assistance at many stages in the project.

I appreciate the support of the National Council of the Society. I am also particularly indebted to Mr. Darrel Reid and his associates at the School of Policy Studies, Queen's University, for their assistance in the publication of this book.

Leo Enright

Introduction

This book is intended as an introduction to the night sky and to the joy of observing it carefully.

It is for those who have no previous background in astronomy, and may be totally unacquainted with any of the stars and constellations that fill our nighttime sky. Perhaps it will be especially useful for young people who, at a summer camp or on a family holiday, are taking serious note of the night sky for the first time.

At most libraries and book stores we can find several very good introductory guides to astronomy, many of them more thorough in their approach than what is presented here. They can be used profitably, and perhaps one of them should be used, as a resource and further reference, if the reader thinks it is necessary to have such additional assistance. The best resource books and guides are listed in Chapter 19.

What is presented here are simple guidelines and observing exercises to be used in conjunction with the star maps that form the core of the text. If used as suggested, these guidelines will assist the novice observer in becoming familiar with the night sky, and they will do it in a way that avoids technical jargon and mathematical detail.

Enjoy the adventure!

Table of Contents

1. Welcome to Astronomy and to the Night Sky — 1

2. Reading the Star Maps and Seeing the Constellations — 10

3. Finding North in the Night Sky — 13

4. Distance, Position, and Brightness in the Sky — 17

5. Names of the Stars — 22

6. The Six Star Maps — 27
   The January-February Night Sky (Map 1) — 27
   The March-April Night Sky (Map 2) — 41
   The May-June Night Sky (Map 3) — 47
   The July-August Night Sky (Map 4) — 55
   The September-October Night Sky (Map 5) — 63
   The November-December Night Sky (Map 6) — 68

7. Tips on Becoming a Better Observer — 74

8. Recording Observations — 77

9. The Importance of Binoculars — 82

10. When to Buy a Telescope — 84

11. Observing the Moon — 88

12. Observing the Planets in 1994, 1995, and 1996 — 99

13. Observing Eclipses in 1994, 1995, and 1996 — 106

14. Observing Meteors and Meteor Showers — 111

15. Observing the Aurora — 115

16. Observing Comets — 118

17. Observing the Zodiacal Light — 120

18. Observing the Sun Safely — 121

19. Where to Get More Information: — 124
    (a) From Joining an Astronomy Club — 124
    (b) From Books — 128
    (c) From Magazines — 131
    (d) From Visiting an Observatory or Planetarium — 132

20. Questions I Always Wanted to Ask About Astronomy — 135

21. Suggestions for Brownies, Guides, Cubs, and Scouts — 140

22. An Appendix of Useful Information — 147

Chapter 1

Welcome to Astronomy and to the Night Sky

Welcome to a new and exciting adventure! It is called astronomy, and it is about the stars, constellations and other objects of the night sky. For hundreds of years, our ancestors have looked at the night sky, used their imagination, saw patterns among the many stars, and enjoyed talking about them. They often wondered what might really be out there where the moon, planets and stars were — far from their earthly homes. The more we, too, look at the night sky the more we will enjoy it. We will soon notice its changes from month to month. Yet there are also many things that we will see staying the same from year to year.

For many years I have enjoyed looking at the sky and showing it to my friends. As you learn more about what is in the sky, you too will enjoy "sharing" the stars, planets, and constellations with other people. You will want to show your friends which constellations are in the southern or in the western sky on a certain night. In fact, you will probably soon surprise yourself because within a few nights you will be able to recognize a dozen or more constellations.

Recently a well-known astronomer wrote that she was twenty years old before she knew that ordinary people with no expensive equipment could actually see the planets, such as Mars, by just looking up in the sky. She had often read about the planets in science fiction, but thought that they could be seen only by astronomers with telescopes. Soon, of course, she learned that some of the planets are brighter than any of the stars in the sky, and are second in brightness only to the moon. That person then started to devote her life to sharing the beauty of the night sky with other people, and teaching them the many things that she was learning.

This is an example of what you, too, can do *without* a telescope or without any equipment at all. There will be more information about this topic later, especially in Chapters 9 and 10. In the meantime, *DO NOT* plan to buy a telecope or other equipment. First get to know the stars and constellations as good friends. Only later when you are very familiar with the night sky, should you consider what equipment you need. Even then, using binoculars should be the next step. Using a telescope will come much later.

Make yourself comfortable under the stars. Enjoy your new-found hobby as you go. Do not become discouraged if you have three or four cloudy nights in a row. Just read a little more of this observing guide and become more familiar with what you will be able to see on the next clear night. The secret to enjoying your observing sessions under the night sky is being prepared for what you will see. Remember the wise old Scouting motto — "Be prepared." That is why you should get to know where in this guide you will find the maps and the descriptions of what you can see on a certain night.

The Basic Motions of the Sky

Before we start using the star maps, we should understand something about the apparent movement of the stars in the sky.

What we see in the sky changes all the time because, as we know, the earth is always rotating. Think about what happens during the daytime. The sun in the morning appears to rise in the east. At noon it appears in the southern part of the sky. In the evening it is seen setting in the west. Similarly, on a clear night, you can see a bright star rise above the eastern horizon in the early part of the night. At about midnight (which means the middle of the night) this same star will be up in the southern part of the sky. When the night ends and morning is coming on, the star will be in the western part of the sky, setting as the sun does in the evening. This motion of the sky is sometimes called *apparent motion*, because it is really we on the surface of the earth who are moving. It is like the view seen by passengers on a fast train when they look out the window. The trees seem to be moving quickly past the windows of the train, but we know it is really the passengers and the train that are moving. Studying *Figure 1* will help us to understand the daily motion of the sky.

The stars that we see in the sky also change from season to season. We know that the earth is in orbit around the sun. If we look out into the clear night sky at midnight *in January*, we will see many beautiful bright stars. If we look out at midnight on a clear night *in July*, which is half a year later, we will see many stars too, but they will all be different, because we will be looking in a completely different direction. Study *Figure 2*. This diagram will help us to understand why there are different stars to be seen during the different seasons of the year.

We may also notice that for this view of the sun and the earth we would have to be very far above the northern hemisphere of the sun and the earth. We may also notice, from the diagram, that we are *not exactly* above the North Pole of the earth. The dot showing the North Pole of the earth is slightly to the left of centre on each circle representing the earth. We can see that the North Pole is in the dark half of the earth during the winter

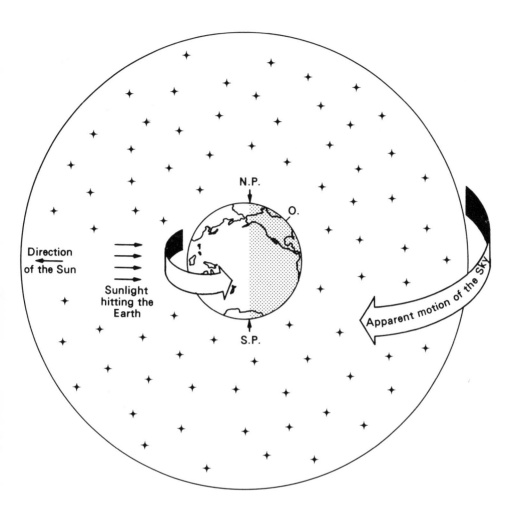

FIGURE 1

This diagram shows the rotation of the earth. All the stars are represented as being on a very large sphere surrounding the earth. N.P. and S.P. represent the earth's North Pole and South Pole. The observer (O.) is on the "night side" of the earth. *Because the earth is turning* and carrying the observer from west to east, the stars *seem* to be moving from east to west, like the trees beside a moving train when a passenger looks out the window. Observers on the other side of the earth do not see the stars at this moment because the sunlight is too bright. They do see the sun. The sun also seems to be moving from east to west because the earth is turning from west to east.

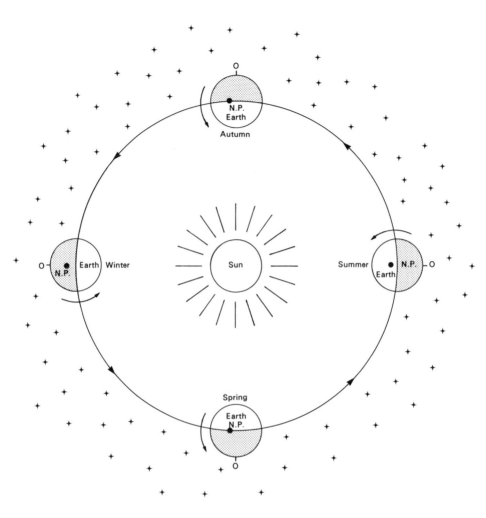

FIGURE 2

This diagram shows an observer (O.) looking out at the nighttime sky at midnight at four times during the year. Notice that this observer will be looking in a completely different direction each time. Therefore, this observer will see different groups and patterns of stars each time. Notice the arrow beside each drawing of the earth. This arrow shows the direction that we would see the earth turning or rotating if we were far, far above the North Pole of the earth or the North Pole of the sun and could look down at the sun and the earth.

season (at the left of the diagram) and in the sunlit half of the earth during the summer season (at the right of the diagram). In fact, the earth is tilted in this way, and this is what causes the seasons of the year.

Therefore, what is in the sky is always changing for *two* reasons. First, the stars that we see in a certain part of the sky change from hour to hour because the earth is rotating, *and* secondly, the stars that we see during the night change from season to season because the earth is in orbit around the sun.

There is another fact that we should know also. Our position on the planet earth is also very important because the earth on which we stand is always hiding half of the sky from us. We have often heard about what is called "the horizon." We can see the sky above it, but all the stars and planets below it are always hidden from us. Refer to *Figure 3*. We can see that if we lived at the North Pole [as shown in *Figure 3(a)*], we would see only the stars that were above the northern half of the earth; we would never see the entire southern half of the sky. The star above the North Pole of the earth, called Polaris or the Pole Star, would be directly overhead. Astronomers say that it is in the zenith — meaning straight overhead.

An observer living at the equator of the earth [as shown in *Figure 3(c)*] might be able to see the Pole Star, but it would be right down at the northern horizon. That same person would also be able to see the stars above the South Pole of the earth but they would be right down near the southern horizon. The stars above the earth's equator would be in the zenith.

Observers in the southern part of Canada are located about at Latitude 43 to 55 degrees North, which is about half-way between the earth's equator and the North Pole. As shown in *Figure 3(b)*, when this observer looks toward the northern horizon, he or she can see the stars above the earth's North Pole. In fact, the Pole Star that is above the earth's North Pole would appear to be up in the sky about half way between the northern horizon and the zenith. This observer *is* able to see the stars that are above the earth's equator, but *is not* able to see the stars that are above the earth's South Pole.

We can understand now why it is difficult to draw a good single map showing all the stars that anyone could see during a whole night. It is best to draw a map showing the stars that we see at one certain time and from one location on the earth. In this booklet we will show only the sky that can be seen from the middle-northern latitudes (those of southern Canada), and there will be six different maps to show the sky at different times of the night during different times of the year.

If we combine the diagram in *Figure 3(b)* with part of the diagram in *Figure 1*, we can understand better why some stars appear to rise and set, whereas other stars are above the horizon all the time and do not rise and set. That is what has been done in *Figure 4*. Study it carefully. It shows the

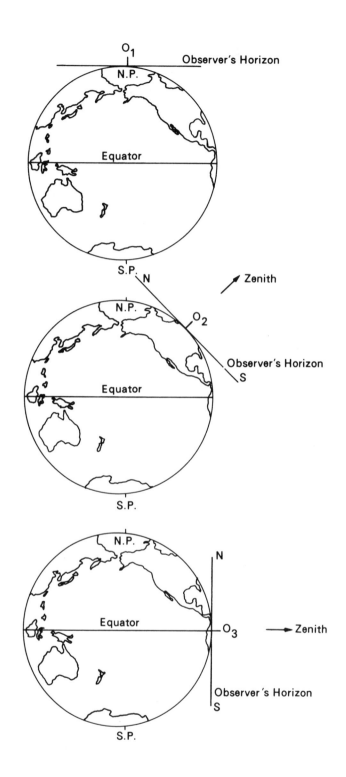

The Beginner's Observing Guide

These three diagrams show that each observer on the surface of the earth has a horizon, and the horizon is different depending on where you live on the surface of the earth. In FIGURE 3(a), the observer is at the North Pole, also called Latitude 90° North. In FIGURE 3(b), the observer is at the mid-northern latitudes (about 45° North). In FIGURE 3(c), the observer is at the earth's equator (0° in latitude).

For the observer (O_1) at the North Pole in FIGURE 3(a), the North Pole Star is directly overhead at a great distance from the earth, and the observer can never see any stars above the southern half of the earth.

For the observer (O_2) at the mid-northern latitudes in FIGURE 3(b), the North Pole Star that is far above the earth's North Pole will appear above his Northern Horizon and he or she will never see the stars that are far above the South Pole.

For the observer (O_3) at the earth's equator in FIGURE 3(c), the North Pole Star that is far above the North Pole of the earth will appear just at the northern horizon or very near the northern horizon. The stars that are far above the South Pole of the earth will be just at the southern horizon or very near the southern horizon. Because the North Pole Star appears so close to the horizon, this observer will never have a very good view of it. However, this observer (O_3) at the earth's equator will be able to see many stars that the other two observers will never be able to see because the southern horizon allows him or her to see many stars that are blocked from view for the other observers.

Notice that there is a relationship between where the North Pole Star is seen and the latitude of the observer. The observer at the North Pole (also called Latitude 90 degrees North) sees the North Pole Star directly overhead (also called 90 degrees altitude). The observer at latitude 45 degrees North sees it as half-way up in the sky (also called 45 degrees altitude). Finally the observer at the earth's equator (also called Latitude 0 degrees) sees the North Pole Star on the horizon or at 0 degrees altitude. It is now easy to see that the observer's latitude on the earth is the same as the altitude or height in the sky of the North Pole Star.

Notice that the position directly overhead or above each observer is called the Zenith. For the observer at the North Pole, the Pole Star is presently only about one degree from the Zenith. There will be very different stars in the Zenith for Observer (O_2) and Observer (O_3).

horizon all around an observer at about Latitude 43 to 55 degrees North, which is approximately the location of most observers in southern Canada. Imagine that you are the observer [O2] at the centre. Above the northern point on the horizon you can see the North Pole Star. It is up in the sky, about half-way between the horizon and the zenith, which is the point directly overhead. When you look to the east, you see stars that are rising above the horizon as the earth rotates. When you look to the west, you will see stars that are setting.

Star A appears in the north-eastern part of the sky, to the right of the North Pole Star but not as high up in the sky as the Pole Star. As the earth rotates, it will later rise higher in the north-eastern sky and will be up near the zenith. Later still it will appear to move down in the north-western sky, but it will not set. It will appear to make a large circle in the northern sky. This is an example of a *circumpolar star* — one that does not set.

Stars B and C have just risen in the east a little while ago. They will rise higher in the sky later in the night as the earth rotates. If the observer watches them long enough, he or she will see them setting in the west. Star B rose a little to the north of the east point on the horizon, and later it will be up very high in the sky, and it will later set at a point to the north of the west point on the horizon. Star C rose to the south of the east point on the horizon. It will later be up in the southern part of the sky but will not be up as high as Star B. Star C will later set at a point south of the west point on the horizon.

We can compare Star B and Star C to certain stars on our six main star maps. Star B is like the bright star Regulus on Map 1. It has just risen in the east. A few hours later it will be much higher in the sky as Regulus is on Map 2.

As a second example, Star B and Star C are like the bright stars Deneb and Altair on Map 3. They have just risen in the east. A few hours later they will be higher in the sky, just as Deneb and Altair are on Map 4. Notice that a few hours later they have started to go down in the west (as seen on Map 5). Finally, later, Deneb and Altair are about to set in the west (as seen on Map 6).

As a third example, Star B is like the bright star Aldebaran on Map 5. Notice that later in the night it is higher in the sky as shown on Map 6. Later it is going down in the west as shown on Map 1, and it is just about to set in the west as shown on Map 2.

As a fourth example, Star A is like the star at the end of the handle of the Big Dipper on Map 1. Later in the night, it is higher in the sky as shown on Map 2. Later still, it is in the north-western part of the sky, as shown on Map 3. This star is called a circumpolar star, as are all the stars in the Big Dipper.

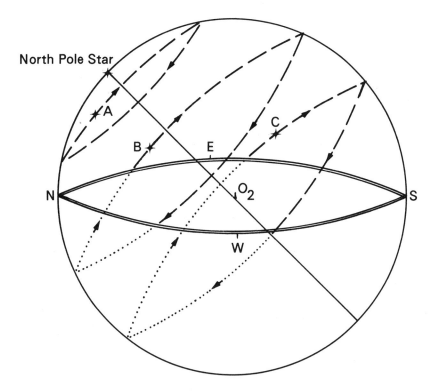

FIGURE 4

This diagram shows the sky above the Observer (O_2) as seen in FIGURE 3(b) on page 6. This observer is at mid-northern latitudes. Try to put yourself at the centre of the diagram in this observer's position. This diagram has the horizon marked with a double line around the observer, and the four directions (or compass points) are marked: N, E, S, and W. Notice that the North Pole Star is seen by the observer to be above the northern part of the horizon.

Three other stars are marked on this diagram.

Star A is in the northern sky. The dashed line near it shows that, as the earth rotates, this star will appear to move upward and to the east of the North Pole Star and then later to move downward making a circle in the sky.

Star B is just rising above the north-eastern horizon. As the earth rotates, it will rise higher and later it will set below the north-western horizon.

Star C has risen a while ago and is in the south-eastern sky. As the earth rotates, it will rise higher in the sky, and later it will set in the western sky south of the western compass point.

On this diagram the dashed lines show the motions of the three stars while they are above the horizon. Star A is always above the horizon, but, of course, we will not see it when the sun rises because of the brightness of the sunlight.

Star B and Star C will both appear to rise and set once each day as the earth turns or rotates, just as the sun appears to rise and set once each day.

Chapter 2

Reading the Star Maps and Seeing the Constellations

Introduction to Our Six Star Maps

Star maps are very useful to those who study the night sky; both beginners and very experienced observers use them all the time.

As we have already seen, the earth is always moving. The stars and all the objects in the sky always *appear to be moving* from east to west in great giant circles around the earth.

In this book, there are six maps of the night sky. They have been drawn for a latitude (the measure of distance from the earth's equator) of about 45 degrees North, which is approximately that for southern Canada and northern United States, though they can be used for the whole mid-Northern area of North America up to the southern parts of the Yukon and Northwest Territories.

In the early evening hours (meaning about dinner time for most people during the winter months, or just after dinner time), you will use one of the six maps.

During the later hours of the evening, or the night, when most people do their observing of the night sky, you will turn to another map — the one that is called the *Night Map* for that time of year.

If you continue to observe the sky during the middle of the night, you will turn to another map that can be used for the hours *after midnight*.

Finally, the *early morning* observers will be able to use another map for the sky before dawn.

In other words it may be necessary to use three or four maps to show the night sky during a whole night.

It is important to note that these maps show the stars and constellations *approximately* as they appear. Some stars shown on the maps near the horizon may not be visible to observers in some locations, particularly those who live in more northerly locations, like the cities of Edmonton or Churchill. On the other hand, some observers in some locations may see some stars that are below the horizon lines on some of the maps; this will be true if you observe the sky from a southerly location, such as one you may visit during a winter vacation.

The six star maps of this guide have titles, as listed below.

Map 1 – January and February Night Map
Map 2 – March and April Night Map
Map 3 – May and June Night Map
Map 4 – July and August Night Map
Map 5 – September and October Night Map
Map 6 – November and December Night Map

The following chart indicates the months and hours of the night when each map is to be used.

	Evening Hours 6 p.m.-8 p.m.	Night 9 p.m.-midnt	After Midnight 1 a.m.-4 a.m.	Early Morning 5 a.m.-7 a.m.
Jan. & Feb.	6	1	2	3
Mar. & Apr.	1	2	3	4
May & June	–	3	4	–
July & Aug.	–	4	5	–
Sept. & Oct.	4	5	6	1
Nov. & Dec.	5	6	1	2

You will have noticed that on the chart there is no map listed for the evening or early morning hours during the months May through August. The reason is that daylight is much longer during these months, and sunlight or twilight will not allow you to observe the starry sky at these times.

By now you will also have noticed that for any particular night, *as the hours pass* and morning gets closer, you can turn to the *following* map to show the stars and constellations that you will see in the sky.

Map Orientation

At the *centre* of each map is the point that astronomers call the *zenith* which was mentioned already in Chapter One. Remember that it is the point directly overhead in the sky.

The heavy black circle that forms the outer edge of each map is the horizon, the line where the earth meets the sky.

Use the maps outdoors where you have a good view of the sky and a good view of the horizon in the directions where you want to look.

When you use one of the maps, be sure you have the correct one, as listed in the chart above, and hold the map out in front of you so that *the direction marked below the horizon (N, E, S, or W) on the map matches the direction in which you are facing (NORTH, EAST, SOUTH, or WEST)*. In other words, if you are facing south, and using Map 1 (January-February Night Map), you should hold it so that the letter "*S*" is at the bottom. If the sky is clear, you should notice the constellations Columba and Lepus above the horizon. Do a quarter-turn to the left. You will now be facing East. You will see the stars of the constellations Canis Major, Hydra, Sextans, and Leo directly in front of you as you turn. Now that you are facing East, you will notice the bright star Regulus, which is part of the constellation Leo, almost in front of you. Practise the same thing turning to the west in order to see other constellations marked on the map.

The Constellation Patterns

As you may already have guessed, constellations are just stars that seem to group themselves into certain patterns or form certain shapes because they appear in the same part of the sky.

In learning to use the star maps, you have already seen several constellations, such as Canis Major, which may or may not appear as a large dog, and Hydra which may or may not appear as a long snake-like monster.

The stars in a particular constellation are not necessarily near or related to each other at all; they just appear to be close to each other. If we were living on a planet in a distant part of the galaxy, the constellation patterns would look completely different from the way they appear to us on the planet Earth.

On the star maps in this book you will notice that many of the bright stars forming the constellation patterns are linked by straight lines. These lines may help you to "see the pattern" in the sky, but *do not worry* if you do not see the pattern that you think you should see. The constellation patters were designed long ago by people with active imaginations. It is more important to see the stars, or most of them, than to "see the constellation patterns".

The names of the constellations are given on the star maps in upper case (capital) letters. A complete list of all 88 constellations is given in the appendix at the end of the book. Of course, from our northern latitudes on the earth, we cannot see all 88 constellations, even over the course of a whole year. Just try to see as many as possible of the constellations named on the star maps.

Other Objects Marked on the Star Maps

The brightest and best-known stars are shown in lower case (small) letters.

The size of the dots indicates the brightness of the stars; the largest dots indicate the brightest stars (such as Sirius, on Map 1); the very smallest dots indicate stars that are just visible to the unaided eye (such as the three stars below the bright star Rigel, on Map 1).

Very small circles of dots indicate some of the well-known star clusters, nebulas, and galaxies. Some of these are not visible to the unaided eye, but can be seen with binoculars.

You will notice that there are dotted lines forming a pathway across all the maps. This pathway shows where the Milky Way is located.

On Map 4 (July - August Night Map), the little asterisk marked GC indicates the direction of the centre of our Milky Way Galaxy.

The following objects are *not* marked on the star maps:

- the moon (See chapter 11)
- the planets (See chapter 12)
- comets, asteroids and meteors.

The reason is that these objects, within our solar system and relatively close to us, continually move and are not located at one fixed position in the sky.

Chapter 3

Finding North in the Night Sky

Locating the Big Dipper and the North Pole Star is the key to finding your directions in the night sky. The Big Dipper is a very large and easily recognized star pattern. Try to introduce yourself to it by facing in a more or less northerly direction. The most easily noticed star pattern in this direction is one that has *seven* very bright stars. These seven stars may seem to form a large dipper standing *on its handle*, or they may seem to make a huge question mark, *if you are looking during a winter evening*. They may seem to form a large dipper standing *on its cup* with the handle pointing upward *if you are looking during a summer evening*. *Figure 5* shows that this pattern of

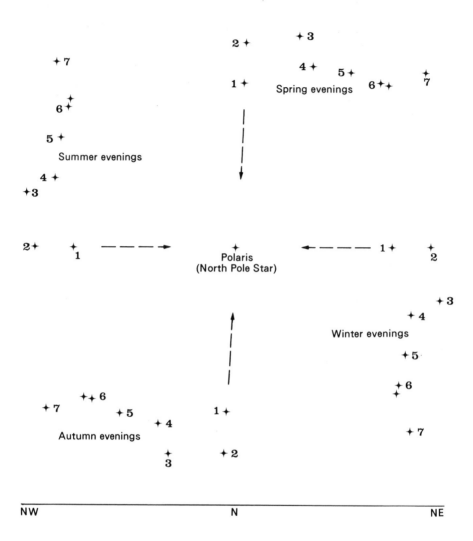

FIGURE 5

This illustration shows approximately the position in the sky of the Big Dipper in the early evening during the four seasons of the year. Notice that at all times the pointer stars of the Big Dipper point to Polaris (the North Pole Star).

The Beginner's Observing Guide

seven stars appears in different positions in the sky depending on the time of year. As you can see, the Big Dipper is standing on its handle *in the winter evenings*; it is standing on the cup *during the summer evenings*; it is high in the sky turned to spill its contents downward *during the spring evenings*, and it is low in the sky turned upward as if sitting on a shelf *during the autumn evenings*. Notice that, no matter what the season is, it is still shaped the same — like a dipper. At certain periods of history, people have also called it The Plough and The Wagon. Whether in your imagination you see a dipper or a plough or a wagon or question mark, or just seven bright stars, does not matter — just as long as you learn to recognize the star pattern.

The Big Dipper is not a whole constellation, but is only a part of the constellation that astronomers call Ursa Major. These are Latin words meaning the Bigger, or Larger, Bear. It is clearly marked on all six star maps. Perhaps as you see some of the fainter stars near the cup of the dipper, you will see why people of long ago were reminded of a huge bear, though it is a strange bear, since it is one with a long tail. Most real bears on earth, of course, do not have long tails, but this is a heavenly bear. If you read the story about how it came to be in the sky, you will find out that a long tail is part of that legend.

Finding the Big Dipper will always be helpful in locating the True North direction. Two of the stars in the cup of the Big Dipper always point to the North Pole Star in the sky. If you are ever lost and need to know directions at night, the two stars in the cup of the dipper that are farthest from the handle are the most important stars in the sky to know. These two stars will easily lead you to the North Pole Star. It is the star that would be almost exactly overhead if you were viewing the sky from the North Pole of the earth.

[Those two famous stars at the end of the cup of the Big Dipper are known by the Arabic names of Dubhe and Merak (pronounced "Doo - Bay" and "May - Rack"). They are the stars number 1 and 2 in Figure 5.]

Draw an imaginary straight line on the sky from the star Merak to Dubhe and extend it on *five times farther*, as shown in *Figure 5*, until you come to the brightest star in the area. This star is Polaris, which means "the Pole Star". You have now found the most important stars in the sky for people of the Northern Hemisphere who want to find their directions. Whenever you see Polaris, you know you are looking North.

In fact, this is also the only star that does not seem to move slowly from east to west as the earth rotates hour after hour during the course of a night. It actually does move in a *very* small circle in the course of one day because it is not *exactly* above the earth's North Pole, but it is so close to the North Pole of the sky that we cannot notice its movement with the unaided eye.

The seven stars of the Big Dipper form one of the most distinctive star patterns in the whole sky and one of the easiest for most people to find and remember, if they live in the Northern Hemisphere of the earth. From all parts of Canada and the northern United States, it is easy to find the Big Dipper on *any clear night* of the year. That is why we can use it as a starting point for finding all the other constellations in the sky at any time of the night or at any time of the year.

Knowing all the stars of the Big Dipper by name, as well as by number, can be useful when you are talking about them. We can name and number these seven famous stars starting with the star at the end of the cup, going around the cup, and then along the handle. (Refer in *Figure 5* to the numbers near the stars of the Big Dipper as seen in the Spring and Autumn evenings.) The Arabic names that have been used for many years are:

1 – Dubhe	5 – Alioth
2 – Merak	6 – Mizar
3 – Phad or Phecda	7 – Alkaid
4 – Megrez	

The star marked near Mizar has a name also. It is called Alcor. It is so close to Mizar that many people do not see it until someone tells them about it. For many years it has been used as a test of good eyesight. Try to find it yourself and test your own eyesight.

Once you can find North in the night sky, you can easily find all the other directions or compass points. Face directly north, that is, toward Polaris (the North Pole Star), which you have just found. Hold your arms straight out as if you were about to begin doing a cartwheel. Your left hand will point to the west and your right hand to the east. Your back will be toward the south.

You have now learned how to find all the compass directions using only the Big Dipper and the star Polaris.

Chapter 4

Distance, Position, and Brightness in the Sky

Measuring the Distance Between Objects in the Sky

Many people are confused about how to measure distance from one star to another star. They sometimes say, "I think it is about two metres from that red star to that bright white one." They forget that metres or centimetres are linear measures of distance. Instead, they should be using an *angular* measure of distance, since thay are measuring the distance apart that the two objects appear to be as viewed from their eyes. Any person can use his or her hand held at arm's length as a guide to *approximate angular measurement.* If you hold up your hand at arm's length, you will see that your little fingernail more than covers the full moon. This means that your little fingernail is a bit more than a half-degree in width. The Full Moon is about a half-degree in diameter. The width of the first knuckle on your little finger is about one degree. The width of your first three fingers extended side by side is about five degrees. The width of the clenched fist is about ten degrees. The width of the first and little fingers extended wide is about fifteen degrees, and the width of the thumb and little finger extended wide is about twenty degrees.

On a clear night, practise these measurements on the Big Dipper. Here is a list of the approximate distances between Dubhe and five of the other stars in this famous group:

1–Dubhe	to	2–Merak	–	5 degrees
1–Dubhe	to	4–Megrez	–	10 degrees
1–Dubhe	to	5–Alioth	–	15 degrees
1–Dubhe	to	6–Mizar	–	20 degrees
1–Dubhe	to	7–Alkaid	–	25 degrees

PRACTISE YOUR SKILLS

(1) On a clear night, estimate the angular distance between any two stars that are in the same part of the sky.

(2)   On a clear night, estimate the angular distance between Dubhe and Polaris (the North Pole Star). (Then check the answer at the end of this chapter.)

Stating the Location of an Object in the Sky

We are all familiar with the four main points on a compass — North, East, South, and West. These four directions are marked on the horizon on *Figure 4.*, and we used them to become familiar with the rising and setting of the stars. We can use these compass directions or *azimuth*, as astronomers call them, to help us state the location of an object in the sky. The horizon around an observer is a large circle of 360 degrees. We start measuring in the north and go around to the east, then south, then west, and finally back to the north where we began. In other words,

North	is	0 degrees.
East	is	90 degrees.
South	is	180 degrees.
West	is	270 degrees.

This means that an object on the horizon in the North-East would be at azimuth 45 degrees, and an object on the horizon in the South-East would be at azimuth 135 degrees. An object at azimuth 158 degrees would be in the South-South-East. An object at azimuth 265 degrees would be almost due West — just 5 degrees south of the West point. An object of azimuth 315 degrees would be in the North-West.

Altitude is measured from any point on the horizon to the zenith, which we know to be the point directly overhead; it is measured in degrees, 0 degrees being exactly on the horizon, and 90 degrees being exactly in the zenith. An object at altitude 45 degrees is half-way between the horizon and the zenith. An object at altitude 30 degrees is exactly one-third of the distance up from the horizon to the zenith, and an object at altitude 60 degrees is exactly two-thirds of the distance up from the horizon to the zenith or one-third of the distance down from the zenith to the horizon.

This system of naming the location of an object in the sky is called the *horizon system* or the *alt-azimuth* system (which is short for *altitude* and *azimuth*). We should know the name to distinguish it from other systems that are used.

Whenever we use this system to state the location of an objects seen in the sky, we must *also* state *the time* when we made our observation.

For example, with the help of Map 1, name the star at azimuth 100 degrees and altitude 25 degrees at 10:00 p.m. local time on February 2. The answer would be Regulus.

PRACTISE YOUR SKILLS

(1) Name the star that is at azimuth 225 degrees and altitude 10 degrees at 10:30 p.m. local time on April 2. (Use Map 2.) (Check the answer at the end of the chapter.)

(2) Name the two stars that are about at azimuth 300 degrees and altitude 15 degrees at 10:00 p.m. local time on June 1. (Use Map 3.) (Check the answer at the end of the chapter.)

(3) On a clear night, choose any three bright stars. Carefully estimate the azimuth and altitude of each one. One hour later, do the same thing. (You may be surprised at the different numbers.)

In this system of naming the location of an object, you should name the azimuth first, then the altitude, and finally the exact time.

Later you will learn other systems of describing the locations of objects in the sky, but this simple system is the one that you should learn first.

Explaining the Brightness of an Object in the Sky

Hundreds of years ago, long before the invention of the telescope, a Greek astronomer invented a system of describing the difference in brightness among the many hundreds of stars in the sky. This man, whose name was Hipparchos, divided the stars that could be seen into six categories. The brightest stars were called category one or *first magnitude*. The faintest stars that a keen-eyed person could see were called category six or *sixth magnitude*. This system is still used today with only a few changes. The higher the number, the fainter the star. Most people with good eyesight can see sixth magnitude stars, if they are out in the country away from the smog and light pollution of a city and if the moon is not in the sky. In a small town or if a Quarter Moon is in the sky, most people can see stars of third or fourth magnitude. From a city or with a Full Moon in the sky, only first magnitude stars are usually seen, that is, stars such as Deneb, Spica, Altair, and Aldebaran. (These four stars are marked on the star maps.)

One change that has been made in this old system is the addition of numbers lower than one. A few *very* bright stars, like Arcturus, Vega, and Capella, are given magnitude numbers zero (0) and minus one (-1). Sirius, the brightest star of all, is given the magnitude number -1.46. Some of the planets are even brighter than this. Jupiter is often brigher than -2. Sometimes Venus is brighter than -4. On this scale the full moon would be brighter than -12, and the sun brighter than -26.

At the other end of the scale, very faint objects have higher numbers. The planet Neptune is a magnitude 8 object, and Pluto is about magnitude 14; it is extremely faint.

Here is a list of examples of stars of certain brightnesses:

Magnitude		
0	–	Capella (in Auriga) (Maps 1, 2, 5, and 6) *and* Vega (in Lyra) (Maps 3, 4, 5, and 6)
1	–	Aldebaran (in Taurus) (Map 1, 2, 5, and 6) *and* Spica (in Virgo) (Maps 2, 3, and 4)
1.5	–	Castor (in Gemini) (Maps 1, 2, 3, and 6)
2	–	Polaris (North Pole Star) (All Maps)
2.5	–	Alpha Pegasi (Star in the Square of Pegasus that is farthest from Andromeda) (Maps 1, 4, 5, and 6)
3	–	Phad (Star Number 3 in Big Dipper) (Figure 5 and All Maps)
3.5	–	Alpha Trianguli (Star in the triangle that is nearest to the constellation Aries) (Maps 1, 5, and 6)
4	–	Mu Andromedae (Star below the galaxy which is below the letter "n" in the word Andromeda on Map 5)
4.5	–	Delta Ursae Minoris (In the handle of the Little Dipper the star which is next to Polaris) (All Maps) *and* Theta Leporis (Star at the end of curving row of stars in upper part of constellation Lepus (Maps 1 and 6)

You will notice that almost all the stars on our star maps are between magnitude 1 and magnitude 4.5. Star atlases, of course, can show you fainter stars. Some atlases show stars as faint as magnitude 6; some show 7 or 8; a few star atlases show stars as faint as magnitude 9 or 10, but when we want to show stars that faint, there are many hundreds of thousands of stars to show.

PRACTICE YOUR SKILLS

(1) On the next clear night, choose any fairly bright star (other than one of those listed above). Estimate its brightness — by comparison with one or more of the stars on the list above, such as Capella, Polaris, or Phad. (If its brightness is about half-way between that of Polaris and Phad, it is about magnitude 2.5.) (Repeat the exercise several times.)

   If you do this exercise regularly, you will become more aware of the magnitude of stars, and you will be more able to estimat the brightness of *any* star.

(2) Ready for a challenge? On a clear night observe the seven stars of the Big Dipper. (a) Which is the faintest? (b) Which one is the brightest? (Check answers at the end of the chapter.)

Later you will also learn about stars that vary or change in brightness. There are many such stars, called *variable stars*, which have *noticeable* changes in brightness. Two very good examples are Algol in Perseus (See Maps 1, 2, 5, and 6), and Mira in Cetus (See Maps 1, 5, and 6). Try to find and observe these two stars as often as you can. Algol is easily seen with the unaided eye, and Mira is sometimes seen in this way and sometimes requires binoculars. Before long you may start to notice changes in the brightness of these two famous stars, and maybe even in the brightness of other stars.

   A list of the 30 brightest stars is given on page 149, and a list of 10 variable stars that can be observed "naked-eye" is given on page 150.

[Answers to **PRACTICE YOUR SKILLS** questions:

   Distance: (2) 29 degrees. Saying "30 degrees" is close enough.
   Location: (1) Sirius
                 (2) Castor and Pollux
   Brightness: (2) (a) Megrez is noticeably fainter than Phad.
                       (b) The three brightest are Dubhe, Alioth, and Alkaid.
                              They are almost the same brightness! It was a challenge!]

Chapter 5

Names of the Stars

Long ago people who watched the night sky gave names to the brightest of the stars. Often they used the names of animals or heroes of their mythology for the stars, just as they did for the constellations. (We have already noted in Chapter 2 some constellation names.) Sometimes stars received their names from the parts of the constellation in which they were found; for example, there are star names which mean "the horse's foot" and "the lion's tail".

In modern times many more stars have been given their own designation, but we still use some of the names that were used hundreds or even thousands of years ago.

The beginner should not worry about having to learn hundreds of star names. It would be wise to become familiar with the twenty or so bright stars that have their own proper names, as shown on the star maps in this book. Most of them are seen in the sky for several months at a time and are found on several of the star maps. The name, and place in the sky, of these stars can be gradually learned as the constellations are recognized, and as you become familiar with the sky in general.

The following information explains how the stars have received their names over the years. Reading it will help you understand the star maps and atlases that you will use in the future.

1. Bright Stars with Proper Names

The very brightest stars have their own proper names, such as Sirius, Capella, Vega, Rigel, and Aldebaran. One modern book lists over 250 stars that have individual names, but only about 50 of these are commonly used.

As noted in Chapter 3, the seven stars of the Big Dipper have Arabic names. Many star names begin with "al", an Arabic word which is like the English word "the". It is found in the names Algol, Altair, Alcor, and many others. Besides Arabic, ancient Greek and Latin names are given to some stars, like Sirius, Capella, Castor and Pollux.

2. The Bayer System of Star Names

In the year 1603, a German astronomer, Johann Bayer, published a star atlas which used a system of naming stars that is still used today. In the Bayer System, the stars in each constellation are named, usually in order of brightness, with the letters of the Greek alphabet. This alphabet has 24 letters and begins with "alpha", "beta", "gamma", ... The complete alphabet is given in the appendix on page 153. The full name of a star in this system is the Greek letter followed by the constellation name (in the Latin possessive form). "Alpha Centauri", for example, is the brightest star in the constellation Centaurus. "Beta Cygni" is the second brightest star in Cygnus. "Gamma Cassiopeiae" is the third star designated in Cassiopeia. This system is used to identify several hundreds of the "naked-eye" stars. It is used in all star atlases.

3. The Flamsteed Number System

Another very common way to identify stars is to use the Flamsteed Number System. It is named after John Flamsteed, a British astronomer who invented the system in the early 1700's. In this system the stars in each constellation are numbered from west to east. The full name of a star in this system is the number followed by the constellation name (in the Latin possessive form). An example is "61 Cygni", a well-known star in the constellation Cygnus. This system is used to identify several thousand stars, and it also is found in all star atlases.

4. Stars From the Catalogues

For the faint stars that are not named by any of the above systems, astronomers refer to one of several catalogues of stars that list many thousands of stars. Usually, two or more letters are used to identify the catalogue; then the star's number is given according to its listing in the catalogue.

One such catalogue is the Henry Draper Catalogue. An example of a star is HD186882. The position of this star can be found by checking in that catalogue.

Another is the Smithsonian Astrophysical Observatory Star Catalogue. An example of a star from its listings is SAO48796.

Many double stars are listed in Aitken's General Catalogue of Double Stars. An example of a star found in this listing is ADS12880.

These three numbers all identify the same star which can be found in the constellation Cygnus. Many stars, like this one, are listed in several different catalogues.

5. The Variable Star Identification System

Stars known to be variable, that is, to have changes in their brightness, have a very different system of identification from other stars. Within each constellation variable stars are given a single letter designation such as R, S, or T, or a double letter designation such as RR, RS, or RT. In a few constellations, such as Orion, which has hundreds of variable stars, some of them are designated by a number. In that case the letter "V", meaning "variable", is used, followed by a number. (One such example is the variable star "V351 Orionis" which is found near the belt of Orion.) Whether the variable star has a single letter, a double letter, or a V-plus-number designation, it is followed by the name of the constellation (in the Latin possessive form). Three well-known examples of variable stars are R Leonis, RR Lyrae, and T Tauri; they are found, of course, in the constellations Leo, Lyra, and Taurus. Several books, such as those recommended in Chapter 19, give further details about the naming of variable stars.

The maps in this book use *only* the first method of naming the stars, that is, the proper names for the brightest stars.

The star maps and star atlases, that you will be using in the future, usually identify the bright stars in two or three different ways on the same map. For example, the star Capella is usually named, as in this book, and also identified as "Alpha" (using the Bayer System since it is the brightest star in the constellation Auriga), and also "13" since that is its Flamsteed number. Betelgeuse, found in this book on maps 1, 2, and 6, is identified on most star maps also as "Alpha" (using the Bayer System) and "58" since that is its Flamsteed number.

Beginners should become familiar with the names of the brightest stars shown on the star maps in this book, and should be aware that the above systems are used on other star maps and in star atlases.

As you use star atlases, such as those recommended later in this book, you will gradually become familiar with more star names and with other ways of identifying stars.

Chapter 6

The Six Star Maps

The January-February Night Sky (Map 1)

Constellations and Naked Eye Objects

The following information is about what you can expect to see in the night sky during January and February and at other times when you use Map 1.

Since you have read Chapter Two, you should already know how to use the star maps.

You are now expected to use Map 1 as your guide in preparing to observe at the times indicated on the star map, and you should take Map 1 (and the other maps in this book too) with you when you go outdoors to observe.

Since you have read Chapter 3 you should now also be able to find the Big Dipper in the northern sky. You will see that it is standing up on its handle. Use it to locate Polaris (the North Pole Star).

Ursa Minor If you are observing under clear dark skies and away from the light pollution of a city, you will be able to see that there is a curving row of stars extending down and bending slightly to the right from the star Polaris, as shown on Map 1. This is called the Little Dipper. You will notice several things about this "dipper": (1) it is smaller than the Big Dipper (that you learned about in Chapter 3), (2) most of the stars are fainter than the stars in the Big Dipper, (3) the two dippers seem to face each other, (4) the handles and cups of the two dippers point in opposite directions, and (5) the handles of the two dippers are bent but they are not bent in the same way. You will notice that, besides Polaris, there is another bright star in the Little Dipper. It is at the end of the dipper's cup, and is known as Kochab (pronounced "coe-cob"). It is the one marked by the large dot below the letter "o" in the words "Ursa Minor" on Map 1.

This dipper is part of the constellation called Ursa Minor (Latin words for Smaller or Little Bear). Here is another bear with a long tail that was put in the sky. It also invites us to learn the story from mythology about why it was put in the sky and why it had this strange feature.

Draco   Perhaps you will be able to see some of the stars that form the constellation Draco, the dragon. As Star Map 1 shows, the tail of this huge animal curls between the two dippers that you have just been observing, and its head now points downward toward the northern horizon. You will notice that one of the bright stars in the dragon's tail is about half-way between Kochab in Ursa Minor and Mizar in Ursa Major. This star, which is called Thuban, is famous because about 3000 years ago it was known as the North Pole Star. If you do not have a good view of the head of Draco, wait until later in the year. Then it will be higher in the sky and easier to see.

Cassiopeia   While facing north, trace a line from the star Mizar (in the handle of the Big Dipper) to Polaris and then extend the line the same distance toward the west until you see what looks like a large letter "W" tilted on its right side. These five bright stars that seem to form the letter "W" or "M" are of almost equal brightness. They are the brightest stars of the constellation Cassiopeia. You may also notice that they are within a hazy band of soft light that crosses the sky — the Milky Way. This whole area of the sky contains constellations with the names of characters from Greek mythology, particularly from the story of the hero Perseus. Besides the hero Perseus himself, there is Andromeda, the princess whom he saved from a sea monster, and also her mother, Queen Cassiopeia, and her father, King Cepheus.

Using their imagination, the people of long ago saw not just a letter "W" or "M", but the image of Queen Cassiopeia sitting on her throne in the sky. Most modern observers, however, do not try to see a royal family, but look for simple patterns like letters of the alphabet, or squares, or triangles.

Cepheus   Near Cassiopeia (as shown on Star Map 1) and between the "W" and the northern horizon are the stars of the constellation Cepheus. The ancient people may have seen a king sitting on a throne. To us it looks like five bright stars forming a toy house that is tilted to one side, with the peak of its roof pointing toward Polaris. The constellation Cepheus is partly in the Milky Way.

Andromeda   The king and the queen were the parents of the Princess Andromeda, the rescued maiden in the story of the hero, Perseus. This famous constellation is easily found by tracing a line from Polaris out to the middle of Cassiopeia's "W" and extending it on further about the same distance. As you can see, this brings you westward to a long, slightly curving line of bright stars. Three of them are very bright and stand up from the horizon. Near them is another curving line of stars that are not nearly as bright and will not be easily seen if you live near a city with bright lights.

The most famous object in this area of the sky is the great Andromeda Galaxy, which is shown on Star Map 1, below the first "A" in the word "Andromeda". This galaxy is a member of the group of galaxies that our own Milky Way Galaxy belongs to, and it is the nearest spiral galaxy. It is only 2.4 million light-years away from our galaxy! (A light-year is the distance that light travels in one year, moving at a rate of 300,000 kilometres per second.) If observing conditions are good, you can see the Andromeda Galaxy with the unaided eye. It looks like a fuzzy smudge of light or a small fingerprint on the sky. If you are able to see it, remember that you are looking at a galaxy containing several hundred billion stars and some of them are like our own sun. Remember, too, that the light from all those stars has taken over two million years to reach your eyes.

Pegasus Moving downward from Andromeda's curving line of bright stars, you may see near the western horizon part of the Great Square of Pegasus, a constellation that appeared to the ancient peoples as a huge winged horse that was part of the story told about another one of the heroes of mythology. As you can see from the star maps, one of the stars of Andromeda is also part of the Square of Pegasus, showing that two different constellations can sometimes claim the same star. If your view of the western horizon is not good, because of trees or light from a nearby city, you will not see all of the Square of Pegasus. You will have to wait until later in the year to have a better view of this large constellation.

Perseus As you move your eyes upward along the line of bright stars in Andromeda, you will come to the bright stars of Perseus. You could also find it if you follow along the Milky Way from Cepheus to Cassiopeia and then move further upward. Rather than seeing Perseus as a great strong hero who rescued the Princess Andromeda, most people nowadays see another curving row of bright stars as shown on Map 1, but this row of stars is not as long as the one in Andromeda.

Not far from this row of stars is the famous slightly reddish star called Algol, which is also marked on the star maps. This is one of the very first stars that was noticed to be variable, that is, to change in brightness. It has a regular period of such changes, fading noticeably every 2.9 days, but it is still easily visible to the unaided eye when it is at its minimum brightness. Try to take note of it every night when Perseus is visible and you may soon start to notice the fading or "winking" that occurs every 2.9 days.

From a good observing location, you will be able to observe a cluster of stars located about half-way between Perseus and Cassiopeia and also marked on the star maps. With binoculars you can see that this is really a double cluster — two groups of many beautiful stars.

Auriga Following further along the Milky Way from Cassiopeia and Perseus, you come to Auriga, high overhead. This constellation has five bright stars. The brightest of them is Capella (meaning "the little goat"). This very bright star, as shown on the star maps, has three fainter stars near it, as though they are kids gathered around a mother goat. In fact, these three stars are often called "The Kids". Amid the five bright stars that form the body of Auriga (a Latin word meaning "the charioteer") you will notice on the star maps that there are three special objects. These are three open clusters of stars, called M36, M37, and M38. They can easily be seen in binoculars.

Orion Moving down from the overhead point toward the *southern* horizon, your eyes will feast upon the largest collection of very bright stars found anywhere in the sky. Midway between the zenith and the horizon is the huge distinctive constellation — Orion, the Hunter. This is a star pattern that really does resemble a mighty giant. Its many bright stars help us, like the people of long ago, to see the image of a great hero charging across the sky. Two bright stars (Betelgeuse and Bellatrix) form his shoulders, and two more (Saiph and Rigel) show his knees. Two of these (Betelgeuse and Rigel) are marked on the maps. The three stars of his belt are in a straight line, and below his belt in the area of his sword, we can see, among the stars, the glowing mass of hydrogen gas that astronomers call M42 and M43. This region has been studied carefully for many years, since it is a very active area where new stars are being born and where variable stars are monitored by keen observers. Take note of "Orion's sword" whenever you get the chance, whether it is with the unaided eye, binoculars, or a small telescope. You will find it a very interesting area of the sky, especially if you are using binoculars.

Canis Major Following the stars of Orion's belt in a straight line toward the left (or the southeast) brings you to the constellation Canis Major (Latin words for the Larger or Bigger Dog), with the steely white star Sirius that some people say forms the eye of the dog. This star is the brightest star in the whole sky and for over a hundred years astronomers have known that it has a companion star, though this companion is too close to the primary star to be easily seen in a small telescope. Sirius is also interesting because it is among the ten closest stars to our sun. Its distance from us is about 8.6 light-years, meaning that it is closer than any other star that can be seen with the naked eye from the northern latitudes of the earth.

Besides Sirius, Canis Major has several other stars that are among the brightest 50 stars in the sky. Try to view all the stars of Canis Major that are marked on the star maps and try to arrange them in order of brightness.

It is interesting to know that Sirius was very important to the ancient Egyptians. They looked forward to the rising of Sirius before the sun each year as a sign of the flooding of the Nile River and growth of crops in the coming season.

Taurus Following the three stars of Orion's belt in a straight line to the right (or to the westward) brings you upward and to a very bright reddish star called Aldebaran. It is part of a grouping of stars called "the Hyades". They seem to form the shape of the letter "V", and to the ancient peoples, this looked like the head of a giant bull from one of the legendary stories.The Hyades are shown on the star map just above the first two letters of the word "Aldebaran", although the word "Hyades" is not there.

Moving on further westward past the Hyades, your eyes will come to the famous cluster of stars called "the Pleiades". They are not named on the star map, but they are shown by a tiny cluster of five dots located under the "s" in the word "Taurus". Under good observing conditions, they are easily visible to the unaided eye. Some people call the Pleiades "the Seven Sisters". Many stories were told about them in ancient times. Some people say they can see six individual stars; other people claim they can see seven stars or even more. Test your own eyesight. Can you see six individual stars?

On the star map you will see that a line is drawn from the star Aldebaran to another star to the east of it and also from another star in the Hyades eastward to one of the five brightest stars in Auriga. Notice that these two lines are like the "horns of the bull", and Aldebaran and the star near it are like the "eyes of the bull". On the star map you will see a tiny pattern of dots near the end of one of the "horns of the bull". This indicates the position of the object that astronomer call M1 or the Crab Nebula. This is the remains of a giant supernova explosion in our galaxy that became visible in the year 1054 A.D.. This object can be seen as a small, fuzzy patch of light in binoculars; it cannot be seen with the unaided eye.

Eridanus Below Taurus and to the west of Orion a large area of the sky is filled by the constellation called Eridanus. The ancient peoples saw it as a long, winding river. There are no stars as bright as Aldebaran in this large constellation.

Aries and Triangulum In the area between the Pleiades and the western point on the horizon there are two small constellations, both of which have only three bright stars. About half-way between the Pleiades and the western horizon, as Map 1 shows, the stars of Aries form what lools like a letter "L" written backwards. The brightest of the three bright stars is the one at the top; the second brightest is the one forming the angle; the faintest of the three is the one further down and to the left.

The constellation Triangulum is inside the area bounded by the Pleiades, the stars of Aries, and upper star in Andromeda's row of bright stars. Triangulum is really a very simple constellation. The three stars of the triangle are usually easy to see if observing conditions are good. The most interesting object for binocular observers is M33, a spiral galaxy that is a little more distant than M31. M33 is marked on the star map about half-way between the star forming the sharp point in Triangulum and the middle star of the three brightest stars in Andromeda. M33 looks very different from M31; this spiral galaxy in Triangulum is "face on", meaning that it is oriented so that we can see the "full face" of the galaxy. Do not expect it to be very bright even in binoculars. Most observers find that it is much larger and fainter than they expect it to be.

Pisces and Cetus Below Taurus, Aries, and Triangulum are two large constellations, both of which may be partly hidden below the horizon. Below Aries and Triangulum you may see the constellation Pisces which has two rows of fairly faint stars that seem to be trying to form the letter "V" which has been tipped over on its side. The ancient peoples saw this "V" as a string that held two fish, one on each end. Using your star map, you can see where one fish is located — between the constellations Aries and Andromeda. The other fish, at the other end of the string, is hidden below the horizon. You will need to wait until later in the year to see it.

Stretching out between the area of Eridanus and Pisces is the constellation Cetus, which the ancient peoples saw as a sea monster or whale. In fact, it was often seen as the monster from which the hero Perseus saved Andromeda. If you have good observing conditions, you may note, as the star map shows, that there is a four-sided figure between Aries and Eridanus. This figure forms the head of the monster. A row of faint stars reaches downward to a large oval of brighter stars forming the main body of the creature. At this time of year, part of the main body of Cetus is below the horizon. Later in the year, you may see all of this huge constellation.

The Beginner's Observing Guide

The most interesting star in this area is the one marked "Mira" on the star maps. This is one of the most famous of the variable stars, and one of the first of them to be discovered. At certain times in its cycle it is as bright as the stars in the belt of Orion; at other times it is so faint that it cannot be seen with the unaided eye and you may have trouble seeing it with binoculars. When it is at the bright part of its cycle, it is easy to find because the stars in the "string of Pisces" point, like an arrow, straight toward it.

Gemini If you now look high toward the zenith, and return to the large constellation Auriga, you will be ready to explore the constellations in the eastern part of the sky. From Capella, the brightest star in Auriga, move across the constellation to the two bright stars on the eastern side of the constellation; then move further eastward about twice that distance. You will immediately see two close, very bright stars called Castor and Pollux, almost equal in brightness, though there is a detectable difference with Pollux being slightly brighter. As you can see from the star map, there is an irregular row of stars extending from each stars and toward the constellation Orion. Ancient peoples saw these rows of stars forming the bodies of the twin sons of the god Zeus. They were called Castor and Pollux, the names we give to the two brightest stars in the constellation. Gemini is the Latin word for "the Twins".

Leo From Castor and Pollux, moving eastward toward the horizon, you will notice one star that is much brighter than any other in this area of the sky. This is the star Regulus, the brightest star in the constellation Leo. It is about half-way between Pollux and the eastern horizon. If you have good observing conditions you will also notice extending to its left what looks like stars forming the shape of a sickle or a backwards question mark. Closer to the horizon is a triangle of stars, as shown on Map 1. Together the ancient peoples saw these shapes as forming the body of a huge lion, the one which was slain by Hercules in one of his twelve labours. The "sickle" formed the head and mane of the lion; the triangle formed its hind quarters.

This area of the sky is famous for having a number of galaxies that may be viewed with a small telescope. One of them is marked near the triangle of stars.

Cancer About half-way between Gemini and the "sickle" of Leo, is a group of stars that are known as the constellation Cancer, the Crab. None of the stars in this area is as bright as Castor, Pollux, Regulus, or some of the other stars in Gemini and Leo. You will see from your star map that there are two "deep sky objects" marked in this constellation. They are both star clusters. The larger, brighter one is called M44 or Praesepe or the

Beehive Cluster and it can even be detected with the unaided eye. It is marked on the star map just below the "N" in the word "Cancer". To the unaided eye it looks like a fuzzy patch of light. Binoculars will show dozens of individual stars. The other cluster, called M67, requires binoculars just to see it.

Try to see as many stars as you can in this constellation, but do not worry if your conditions do not allow you to see all of those that are marked on the star map.

Hydra In the area between Cancer and the southeastern horizon, there is a long, winding pathway of stars that make up the constellation called Hydra, the sea-serpent. Most of the stars in this constellation are not very bright. One exception is the star named Alphard, the brightest in the constellation. It is marked on the star map, but its name is not given. It is the star that appears about half-way between Regulus and the three stars that form the small constellation Pyxis down near the southeastern horizon. Those three stars may be difficult to see if trees or lights block the southeastern horizon, but the brightest star in Hydra is easy to see. If you have good dark skies, it should be easy to see the five stars that form the head of the Hydra, as shown on the star map just below the stars of the constellation Cancer.

Canis Minor After finding Leo and Cancer and the head of the Hydra, it is easy to locate Canis Minor (Latin words for the Smaller Dog). Between the bright star Regulus in Leo, which is in the east, and the stars in the belt of Orion, which is in the south, there is only one very bright star. It is Procyon, the brightest star in Canis Minor. As the star map shows, there is only one other bright star in this small constellation. Like Sirius, Procyon also happens to be one of the stars that is near to our solar system.

Monoceros Between Canis Minor and Canis Major is the constellation Monoceros (Latin word for Unicorn). There are no bright stars in this constellation and you may miss it entirely, if you are observing from a location that has city lights nearby. Challenge yourself; try to see all the stars shown on the star map. You will probably not see the shape of a unicorn in the pattern of stars; almost no one does!

Lepus and *Columba* Below Orion are two constellations representing wild creatures. The first one is the area of the sky known as Lepus (the Rabbit). You may under good conditions see all the stars marked on the map. However, if your skies are not very good, you will probably see only about four of them. Also, depending on your southern horizon, you may see all, some, or none of the stars in the constellation Columba (the Dove).

The Great Circle Around Betelgeuse Many people have noticed that in the winter evening skies there are many bright stars, and some of the very brightest seem to form a giant ring around Betelgeuse, the star in the shoulder of Orion. This great ring or circle of stars is made up of Capella, Aldebaran, Rigel, Sirius, Procyon, Castor and Pollux. Such a huge circle of brilliant stars is very easy to find because it has some of the brightest stars in the sky.

PRACTISE YOUR SKILLS

(a) Finding the Bright Stars

The following 12 stars are labelled on Map 1. They are easy to find in a clear sky. Check them off on this list as you find them.

- Sirius (the Dog Star in Canis Major, brightest star in the sky)
- Betelgeuse (the shoulder star in Orion)
- Rigel (the knee star in Orion)
- Aldebaran ("the eye of the bull" in Taurus)
- Castor and Pollux (The Heavenly Twins, the brightest stars in Gemini)
- Procyon (The Little Dog Star in Canis Minor)
- Regulus (brightest star in Leo)
- Capella ("the Goat Star" in Auriga)
- Polaris (the North Pole Star in Ursa Minor)
- Mira (the Wonderful Star in Cetus, a star that varies widely in brightness)
  (This is the one star on the list that may be too faint to see, if it happens to be at the faint part of its cycle.)
- Algol (a star in Perseus; it varies regularly in a period of about 2.9 days)

(b) 10 Interesting Objects for Binoculars

The following is a list of 10 objects that are very interesting to observe, and easy to find in binoculars. They are large and distinctive, and once you see them you will want to return to them many times. They are objects that a beginner should see and recognize before trying for other objects.

- Mizar and Alcor (The second star, counting from the end of the handle of the Big Dipper, along with the nearby fainter star that is shown on the star map, are the famous pair that give a test of good eyesight when viewed with the unaided eye. If you view them with binoculars, you will see that there also is a third star nearby. When viewed with large binoculars or a small telescope, Mizar, itself appears as a double star.)

— M45 (The Pleiades, the famous cluster in Taurus that often appears as six or seven stars to the unaided eye, shows a dozen or more stars in binoculars. The nebulosity around one or more of the stars may be seen in a telescope under good conditions.)

— M44 (The Beehive Cluster in Cancer is a "swarm of stars" in a good pair of binoculars. Enjoy the view.)

— M42 (Using binoculars or a small telescope, observe this nebula below the belt of Orion on a clear, dark winter evening. Notice the swirling mass of gas. Describe or draw the shape that you see. Does it look like a bird, or a small kite, or some such object?)

— M35 (This cluster of stars near the "feet of Gemini" is much smaller than M44. You may notice another fainter cluster of stars nearby.)

— Hyades Star Cluster (This huge cluster of bright stars near Aldebaran forms "the head of Taurus, the Bull". You can see some of these stars with the unaided eye. In binoculars, you will see dozens of stars, and in a small telescope, you may have to move the intrument a little in order to see all of them; otherwise they will not all fit into the field of view.)

— NGC869 and 884 (This Double Cluster in the Milky Way between Perseus and Cassiopeia will give you a very interesting sight in binoculars. Under good observing conditions, it can easily be seen naked-eye.)

— M41 (Not far below Sirius you will find this cluster of stars. Do you notice, in your binoculars, that there is one bright star near the centre of the group? What colour is it?)

— M31 (This famous Andromeda Galaxy is very distinctive in binoculars, and very easy to find since it can be seen with the unaided eye.)

— M33 (The first time you try, you may find it difficult to see this large galaxy in Triangulum, because it may be larger than you expect it to be.)

(c) Deep Sky Objects for the Small Telescope

The following list of 22 objects is a handy summary of all the deep sky objects marked on Map 1 (each indicated with a tiny circle of five dots). They are objects far beyond our solar system, that is, galaxies, star clusters, or nebulae that may be seen with a small telescope or good-quality binoculars. A few of them can be seen easily with the unaided eye. The ones that can be seen in this way are mentioned below. Some of them will be easy for the beginner to find; others will be more difficult.

> This list of objects should be attempted *only after* completing the previous lists and becoming familiar with the use of a star atlas and a small telescope.

The names of many "deep sky objects" begin with the letter "M". This means that the object is from what is called the Messier Catalogue of 110 deep sky objects. The French astronomer, Charles Messier, compiled the original version of this catalogue or list in the late 1700's; he was, in fact, drawing up a list of objects that could possibly be confused with comets because his main interest at the time was in searching for comets. Even though others added more objects to the list and there have been minor changes to it, the "M-objects" or "Messier objects" are still the most common of the deep sky objects observed by amateur astronomers. In fact, some amateurs have observed all of Messier's objects with binoculars.

The letters "NGC" indicate that the object is listed in The New General Catalogue of Non-stellar Astronomical Objects, originally published in 1888. Of course, that list of over 7800 deep sky objects (galaxies, star clusters, and nebulae) is over 100 years old, and is certainly no longer a new list, but the name and number are still used to identify those hundreds of objects. Some are bright enough to see naked-eye, as noted below; others are much fainter.

Check off each object when you have observed it.

- M41 (a cluster of stars in Canis Major, just south of the star Sirius)
- M47 (a cluster of stars just east of Canis Major)
- M93 (a cluster of stars found on map just below the "M" in the words Canis Major)
- M1 (a supernova remnant called the Crab Nebula, an expanding gas cloud in Taurus)
- M35 (a cluster of stars in Gemini)
- M37, M36, M38 (the three clusters of stars in Auriga)
- M45 (the famous Pleiades star cluster, easily seen naked-eye)
- M44 (the famous Beehive Cluster in Cancer; a naked-eye object)

- M67 (a small fainter star cluster in Cancer)
- M66 (a spiral galaxy marked below the triangle in Leo; nearby is another spiral galaxy, M65)
- M51 (the famous Whirlpool Galaxy in the constellation Canes Venatici; it is marked on the star map just below the end star in the handle of the Big Dipper.)
- M106 (a galaxy in Canes Venatici; it is marked on the map half-way between the cup of the Big Dipper and the stars of Canes Venatici)
- M63 (a galaxy in Canes Venatici; marked above the "C" in Canes Venatici
- M101 (a large "face-on" galaxy in Ursa Major; marked above the end star in the handle of the Big Dipper)
- M81 (a spiral galaxy in Ursa Major; it is marked between the cup of the Big Dipper and the constellation Camelopardalis; near it may be seen the irregular galaxy M82, a fine sight in a small telescope)
- M31 (the famous Andromeda Galaxy; shown below the first A in the word Andromeda; it may be seen naked-eye under good conditions)
- M33 (a large "face-on" galaxy in Triangulum; it has been called the Pinwheel Galaxy; like M31, one of the nearest galaxies to our Milky Way)
- M39 (an open star cluster near the star Deneb which is very low near the northwestern horizon. It will be better seen later in the year)
- M42 (the famous Orion Nebula; it is seen naked-eye below the "belt of Orion"; very fine object in a small telescope)
- NGC869 (part of the Double Cluster, along with NGC884; formerly called "h and X Persei; may be seen naked-eye; marked on the map half-way between the constellations Perseus and Cassiopeia; dazzling in a small telescope)

The March-April Night Sky (Map 2)

Constellations and Naked-Eye Objects

For viewing objects in the sky during the times given on Map 2, you may use the following as your guide.

Some of the constellations previously seen in the western sky and marked on Map 1 have now disapppeared below the western horizon. Certain other constellations, that you did not previously see, have now appeared above the eastern horizon.

The constellations that are now no longer seen in the western sky are Cetus, Pisces, Pegasus, Andromeda, Triangulum, Aries, Eridanus, Lepus, and Columba.

The constellations that have appeared in the east are Bootes, Virgo, Corvus, Crater, and Corona Borealis. Parts of Hercules and Lyra are also visible in the northeast, as well as part of Serpens in the east, and Antlia in the Southeast.

With some adjustment, you can use the description of the constellations for Map 1, if you remember that all of them have moved westward. Use the following section for constellations and naked-eye objects that have risen in the east.

The Constellations of the Eastern Sky

Having found the Big Dipper in Ursa Major, as you have done previously, you can now proceed to all of the constellations of the eastern sky. You will have noticed that the Big Dipper is now high in the northeastern sky.

Bootes Follow the curve of the stars in the handle of the Big Dipper downward and to the right. This will bring you to a bright reddish yellow star called Arcturus, the brightest star in the northern half of the sky. Northward from this star is a pattern of stars that the ancient peoples associated with a herdsman or shepherd called Bootes. Many people nowadays see, not a person, but the shape of a large kite. If you have good observing conditions, you may notice five or six fairly bright stars enclosing the area of "the kite". Near Arcturus, as the star map shows, you will probably see five other stars that seem to make a stand for this kite which has been tipped over on its side. On the star map, they are the stars that surround the "A" in the word "Arcturus".

Virgo Retrace the curving line from the Big Dipper's handle to Arcturus and continue it on to the brightest star in the southeastern sky. This is Spica, the brightest star in the constellation Virgo. This large constellaion was seen by the ancients as a goddess. As the star map shows, you may recognize a pattern of stars that seem to form a large box with two curving lines extending out from it toward the constellation Leo which is higher in the sky and which was described previously. Virgo is an area of the sky that contains many distant galaxies.

Corvus and *Crater* Low in the southeastern sky and to the right from the star Spica is a distinctive pattern of four bright stars that seem to form a box tilted on its side. The two upper stars are almost in line with Spica. This pattern is called Corvus, a constellation that long ago was seen as a crow. This bird was drinking from a large cup situated nearby. Slightly up and to the right from Corvus is Crater, the drinking cup. It seems to be tilted to the left toward the crow which is drinking from it. Crater does not have any stars as bright as the four main stars of Corvus, and it may be difficult to recognize the pattern, if sky conditions are not good. You will notice, too,that these two star patterns, Corvus and Crater, seem to be riding on the back of Hydra, the sea monster whose body is shown by the long row of stars across the sky just above the southeastern horizon.

Corona Borealis If you move back to the eastern sky and look below the top end of "the kite" of Bootes you may see a pattern of stars that almost forms a circle. It is just rising in the east-northeast, and as the star map shows, is between Bootes and Hercules which has partly risen. Corona Borealis (Latin words for the Northern Crown) does somewhat resemble a crown. Some of the stars are like gems on a crown, and the brightest gem of all is called Alphecca. This star is marked on the star map, but it is not labelled. Some astronomers remember Corona Borealis as an area that has several famous variable stars.

PRACTISE YOUR SKILLS

(a) Finding the Bright Stars

The following 14 stars are labelled on Map 2. They are very easy to find in a clear sky since they are among the brightest of the stars. Check each one as you identify it.

- Sirius (the famous Dog Star in Canis Major, brightest star in the sky)
- Betelgeuse (the red giant, shoulder star in Orion)
- Rigel (the bright white knee star in Orion)

- Aldebaran (the "eye of the bull" in Taurus)
- Algol (famous variable star in Perseus with a regular period of 2.9 days)
- Castor and Pollux (the Heavenly Twins, brightest stars in Gemini)
- Procyon (the Little Dog Star in the constellation Canis Minor)
- Regulus (brightest star in Leo)
- Polaris (the North Pole Star in the constellation Ursa Minor)
- Capella ("the Goat Star" in Auriga)
- Arcturus (very bright, red giant star in Bootes)
- Spica (brightest star in Virgo)
- Vega (brightest star in Lyra)

(b) 8 Interesting Objects for Binoculars

Use the same checklist as for Map 1 (pages 35-36) with the following exception. Delete the last two objects, M31 and M33, because the area of the sky where they are found has now set.

(c) Deep Sky Objects for the Small Telescope

There are 27 Deep Sky Objects shown on Map 2.

> Before attempting to observe them, be sure to read the information above the list on pages 37-38.

Each object is indicated by a tiny circle of dots. They are the same as those shown for *Map 1* with the following exceptions:

(a) M31, M33 and M39 are *not* shown since they have set in the west.

(b) Since the areas of Coma Berenices, Virgo, and Hercules are up in the eastern sky, these *eight* objects are shown:

- M89, M84, and M58 (three galaxies in the constellation Virgo) (A small telescope can show many other galaxies, besides these three, in the area of Coma and Virgo where these three are marked. In fact, there is a large cluster of galaxies in this region of the sky.)
- M104 (a distinctive galaxy called "the Sombrero" because of its unusual appearance. Marked on the map between Virgo and Corvus)

- M13 (a large globular cluster in Hercules, marked on the map above the letter "S" in the word "Hercules")
- M92 (a globular cluster in Hercules, maked on the map above the first "E" in the word "Hercules")
- M3 (a globular cluster in Canes Venatici, marked on the map between the words "Bootes" and "Canes Venatici")
- M5 (a globular cluster in Serpens Caput, marked on the map just above and slightly to the right of the "E" indicating the eastern horizon)

The May-June Night Sky (Map 3)

Constellations and Naked-Eye Objects

For viewing the sky during the times given on Map 3, you may use the following as your guide.

You will notice that some of the constellations previously seen in the western sky and marked on Map 2 have now set below the western horizon. Certain other constellations, that you did not previously see, have now risen above the eastern horizon.

The constellations that are now no longer seen in the western sky are the "winter constellations": Orion, Canis Major, Canis Minor, Monoceros, Taurus, and part of Auriga.

The constellations that have appeared in the east are Hercules, Lyra, Cygnus, Aquila, Ophiuchus, Serpens, Libra, Scorpius, Sagitta, Delphinus, and Scutum.

For *most of the constellations shown on Map 3*, you can use the descriptions given for Maps 1 and 2, with one important adjustment. You must remember that all of them have moved westward a certain amount.

Use the following section for constellations and naked-eye objects that have risen in the east.

The Constellations of the Eastern Sky

Following the handle of the Big Dipper away from its cup, as you did previously, you come again to the very bright star Arcturus, which is now high in the sky. In fact, it is almost directly overhead. You will be able to use Arcturus as a guide to the constellations and stars of the eastern sky.

Hercules Facing east and directing your view downward and to the left from Arcturus, you will see first the semi-circle of stars called Corona Borealis, and then the large constellation named Hercules. The most distinctive pattern in this constellation is a group of four stars called "the Keystone", found on the star map above the last four letters of the word "Hercules". The ancient peoples recognized in this area the body of the great hero named "Heracles" or "Hercules", who was known for his strength and his success in performing twelve enormous tasks that no ordinary person would attempt.

In this area on the star map you will see marked two deep-sky objects, both of them globular clusters. They are called M13 and M92. Notice that this constellation extends down toward Ophiuchus. The line drawn in that direction stops at the star called Alpha Herculis or Ras Algethi. It is a famous double star that can be resolved into its two parts in a small telescope.

Lyra Continuing further downward toward the eastern horizon and slightly to the left you come to a very bright star named Vega. It is the brightest of the several naked-eye stars that form a distinctive parallelogram pattern known as the constellation Lyra. Actually, you will see that the parallelogram is below Vega, and Vega is part of a small triangle of stars. The star just to the left of Vega is the one astronomers call Epsilon Lyrae, or the "Double Double", since, in a small telescope, you can see that it is not just a double star, but that each star is itself a double. Many beginning observers also remember Lyra as a constellation that has a variable star which can be easily observed with the unaided eye. It is the star named "Beta Lyrae", and is the one shown on the star map closest to the letter "L" in the word "Lyra".

Cygnus Low in the eastern sky, half-way between Vega and the horizon is the large cross-like pattern of stars named Cygnus, the Swan or the Northern Cross. You can easily see that this cross seems to be tilted on its side. The brightest star named Deneb is at the top of the cross, and the whole constellation is in the Milky Way.

Among the many interesting objects in this constellation is a bright and very beautiful double star named Albireo. It is the star at the "bottom of the cross" or the "head of the swan" — the star that is marked just above the last letter of the word "Cygnus" on the star map. The two stars of this famous double are blue and gold in colour, and they are far enough apart to be clearly distinguished in binoculars.

Aquila Just barely rising above the eastern horizon is the star Altair, the brightest one in the constellation Aquila, the Eagle. This star is among the fifty stars closest to our sun. The constellation pattern will be better recognized later in the year or later in the night when it is higher in the sky.

The Great Summer Triangle The three bright stars that you have just observed, Vega, Deneb, and Altair, are known as the Summer Triangle. During late spring, throughout the summer and even into the autumn these stars dominate the southern part of the sky and are easily recognized.

Ophiuchus and *Serpens* If, instead of moving down from the area of Hercules to Lyra and Cygnus, you move in a more southeasterly direction from Hercules, you will come to the large five-sided pattern of stars in the constellation Ophiuchus. This constellation was known to the ancient peoples as The Serpent Bearer, but nowadays no one sees a person holding a snake. Instead some people call it "The Coffin", because to them it looks like a large box. The brightest star in the constellation, Alpha Ophiuchi or Ras Alhague, is the one shown at the point formed by the star pattern at the left side of the constellation. This constellation contains a number of star clusters, none of which is marked on our star maps.

Extending out on both sides of Ophiuchus are parts of the constellation called Serpens, the Serpent or Snake. This is the only constellation that is broken into two parts. The head of the snake, Serpens Caput, has a row of stars extending upward from Ophiuchus toward Corona Borealis. The snake's tail, Serpens Cauda, extends downward from the southern part of Ophiuchus toward Aquila. The upper part of Serpens contains a well-known globular cluster of stars called M5, which can be seen in binoculars.

Libra   About half-way between Arcturus and the southeastern horizon is the constellation Libra, the Scales, marked by four naked-eye stars. They form a box or square pattern with the two stars on the upper right being the brightest. The one shown closest to the letter "L" in the word "Libra" on the star map appears as a double star in binoculars. It has the interesting Arabic name "Zubenelgenubi". The star at the top of the square, with the equally interesting name "Zubeneschamali" is sometimes reported to appear greenish in colour both when wiewed naked-eye and with optical aid. Look at it carefully yourself, and record what colour you see.

Scorpius   To the left of Libra and just rising above the southeastern horizon is Scorpius, the Scorpion. It is known for its bright red star Antares, a star that is as red as the planet Mars. The name of the star itself means that it is the rival of Mars. Some people claim that the pattern of the constellation actually resembles a scorpion with the bright stars between Antares and Libra forming the claws of the animal and the long row of stars to the lower left of Antares forming the tail. Marked on the star map just to the right of Antares is the cluster of stars called M4, a grouping that can easily be seen in binoculars.

PRACTISE YOUR SKILLS

(a) Finding the Bright Stars

The following 11 bright stars are labelled on Map 3. Check them off as you find them in a clear sky.

- Castor and Pollux (the Heavenly Twins, brightest stars in Gemini)
- Regulus (brightest star in Leo)
- Polaris (the North Pole Star in Ursa Minor)
- Capella ("the Goat Star" in Auriga)
- Arcturus (very bright, red giant star in Bootes)
- Spica (brightest star in Virgo)
- Vega (brightest star in Lyra)
- Deneb (brightest star in Cygnus or the Northern Cross)
- Altair (brightest star in Aquila)
- Antares (brightest star in Scorpius)

(b) 4 Interesting Objects for Binoculars

The following four are among the best of the deep sky objects. You should try to observe them before going on to others.

- M44 (the Beehive Cluster in Cancer with its dozens of bright stars)
- M4 (the globular star cluster in Scorpius just to the west of the star Antares)
- M11 (the open cluster of stars in Scutum; sometimes called the "Wild Duck Cluster")
- M13 (the large bright globular cluster of stars in the "Keystone of Hercules")

(c) Deep Sky Objects for the Small Telescope

The following 22 Deep Sky Objects are labelled on Map 3.

> Before attempting to observe them, read the information above the list on pages 37-38.

- M81 (a spiral galaxy in Ursa Major; it is marked on the star map between the cup of the Big Dipper and the constellation Camelopardalis; near it may be seen the irregular galaxy M82; a fine sight in a small telescope)

- M106 (a galaxy in Canes Venatici; it is marked on the map half-way between the cup of the Big Dipper and the stars of Canes Venatici)

- M66 (a spiral galaxy marked below the triangle in Leo; near it is another spiral galaxy, M65)

- M63 (a spiral galaxy in Canes Venatici; marked on the map above the "N" in the first word of "Canes Venatici")

- M101 (a large "face-on" spiral galaxy in Ursa Major; marked above the end star in the handle of the Big Dipper)

- M51 (the famous Pinwheel Galaxy in the constellation Canes Venatici; it is marked on the star map just below the end star in the handle of the Big Dipper)

- M44 (the famous Beehive Cluster of stars in Cancer; near the middle of the constellation Cancer)

- M67 (another cluster of stars in Cancer; shown south of M44)

- M4 (a globular star cluster in Scorpius; just to the right of Antares)

- M5 (a globular star cluster in Serpens Caput; marked on the map half-way between the words "Ophiuchus" and "Virgo")

- M11 (an open star cluster in Scutum; marked on the map just above the eastern horizon and between the words "Aquila" and "Scutum")

- M27 (a planetary nebula called the Dumbbell Nebula; in the constellation Vulpecula; marked on the star map just above the "G" in the word "Sagitta")

- M89, M84, M58 (galaxies in the constellation Virgo; a whole cluster of galaxies may be found where these three are marked)

- M13 (a large, bright globular star cluster in Hercules)

- M92 (a globular star cluster in Hercules)
- M3 (a globular star cluster in Canes Venatici; marked on the map just below the letter "E" in the word "Bootes")
- M39 (an open cluster of stars near Deneb in Cygnus)
- M104 (the Sombrero Galaxy in the constellation Virgo; marked on the map just above the "R" in the word "Corvus")
- NGC869 (part of the Double Cluster, along with NGC884; formerly called "h and X Persei"; may be seen naked-eye; marked on the star map half-way between the constellations Perseus and Cassiopeia and very low near the northern horizon)
- NGC6960 (part of the Veil Nebula, along with NGC6979; found on the map near the "arm star" of the Northern Cross of Cygnus and low near the east-northeastern horizon; will be seen better later in the year when it is higher in the sky)

The July-August Night Sky (Map 4)

Constellations and Naked-Eye Objects

For viewing the summer sky during the times given on Map 4, you may use the following as your guide.

You will notice that some of the constellations previously seen in the western sky and marked on Map 3 have now set below the western horizon. Certain other constellations, that you did not previously see, have now risen above the eastern horizon.

The constellations that are now no longer seen in the western sky are some of the "spring constellations": Gemini, Cancer, and parts of Leo.

The constellations that have appeared in the east are Delphinus, Equuleus, Pegasus, Andromeda, and parts of Aquarius, and in the south Sagittarius and Capricornus.

For many of the constellations, you may use the descriptions given for Maps 2 and 3, if you remember that all of them have moved westward a certain amount.

The Constellations of the Northern Sky

Having read Chapter 3, you should be able to find the Big Dipper in the constellation Ursa Major. You will notice that it is in the northwest rather than due north, and that it is standing on its cup with the handle pointing upward. The "Pointer Stars" direct you to Polaris, the brightest star in Ursa Minor. You will notice that the Little Dipper is almost standing on its handle with its cup upward and toward the west. The stars of Draco wind between the two dippers and curl high in the sky with the head of the Dragon almost directly overhead. Tracing a line from the middle of the handle of the Big Dipper to Polaris and extending it on an equal distance brings you to the "W" of Cassiopeia, which is well up in the northeastern sky. If observing conditions are good, you will notice that it is in the Milky Way, the great band of millions of stars running across the sky. Below Cassiopeia and just at the northeastern horizon is the constellation Perseus. Above Cassiopeia and partly within the band of the Milky Way are some of the stars of the constellation Cepheus. As the star map shows, Cepheus with its five bright stars looks somewhat like a house that has been tilted to one side with the peak of its roof pointing almost to Polaris. The whole area of sky below Polaris is filled by two constellations that have no bright stars in them; because of this, they can be easily overlooked even though they occupy a fairly large area of sky. They are Camelopardalis, the Giraffe, and Lynx, the Lynx.

The Region of the Summer Triangle Taking the place of the bright star Arcturus that was previously high in the sky is a triangle of bright stars not far from the zenith. (You will see that Arcturus is now well down in the western sky and Spica has almost set at the western horizon.) As Star Map 4 indicates, *Vega* in Lyra, *Deneb* in Cygnus, and *Altair* in Aquila are the trio of brilliant stars close to the zenith. If the sky is dark enough, after twilight has ended, and a bright moon is not interfering, and you are well away from the light pollution of a city, then you will notice something else about this area of the sky. The Milky Way is spread across the sky, running roughly from north to south. In fact, the Milky Way surrounds two of these three stars, completely enclosing the constellations Cygnus, the Northern Cross, and Aquila, the Eagle. The consellation Lyra is just outside the bounds of the Milky Way. We now know that the Milky Way is not a river of milk or a hazy cloud in the sky, but millions of stars; in fact, after the invention of the telescope about four hundred years ago, astronomers first saw what it really was, just as binoculars or a small telescope show us the innumerable stars in this galaxy of ours that we call the Milky Way. As you become more familiar with the sky, you will return to the area of Cygnus many times to explore the fascinating objects that are found there.

Between Cygnus and Aquila you may see four stars that form the small constellation named Sagitta, the Arrow. Near it are three other very small constellations. To the east, as you will see on your star map, are Dephinus, the Dolphin and Equuleus, the Colt. The first of these contains six stars in a pattern that actually does look like a small dolphin leaping out of the water. The second with four very faint stars does not look at all like a horse; in fact, many observers feel fortunate if sky conditions allow them to see any of the four stars. To the north and in the position between Sagitta and the last letter of the word "Cygnus", as shown on the star map, is the very tiny constellation referrd to as Vulpecula, the Fox. It has only one star bright enough to be indicated on our star map. However, it does have one object well known to most astronomers, the deep sky object, M27 or the Dumbbell Nebula, which is an example of a planetary nebula.

The Star Clouds to the South As you move from Altair toward the southern horizon, you will notice, again if conditions are good, that the Milky Way becomes more dense and defined in certain spots. Here there are millions of stars in the central region of our galaxy. The densest regions can be seen in the constellation Scutum, the Shield and in Sagittarius, the Archer, though the Milky Way extends to the right to

The Beginner's Observing Guide

include part of the constellation Scorpius, the Scorpion, which may be partly below your horizon, as shown on the star map. The constellation Sagittarius appears to most people not as a person but as a "teapot", with its spout to the right and handle to the left. As the star map indicates with the letters "GC" (for Galactic Centre) to the right of the spout, the centre of the Milky Way Galaxy is located in this direction. Many examples of nebulae and star clusters are found in this part of the sky.

Ophiuchus and Serpens The two constellations, Ophiuchus, the Serpent Bearer and Serpens, the Serpent, were previously seen low in the southeast. Now they are high in the south and appear to dominate a large region of the sky. Ophiuchus contains a number of interesting star clusters that you can search for with binoculars. Serpens is a divided constellation, as the star map shows, with the head and part of the large snake's body to the right of Ophiuchus and its long straight tail to the left. On the star map, the two parts are labelled Serpens Caput (the Head) and Serpens Cauda (the Tail).

The Remaining Spring Constellations in the West The spring constellations that dominated the southern sky a few months ago are now sinking in the west. Most of Leo, the Lion, is below the horizon. Virgo, with the bright star Spica, is lying along the southwestern horizon, followed by the four stars that form the square of Libra.

The First of the Autumn Constellations Rising in the East Moving down from Cygnus to the eastern horizon, your eyes meet the Great Square of Pegasus. It actually looks like a huge diamond standing on one point just north of the eastern point on the horizon. The bright stars of Andromeda are stretched along the northeastern horizon. The galaxies, M31 and M33, are both close to the horizon and on either side of the "middle star" of Andromeda. Two other constellations that will dominate the southern sky in the autumn are now just on the horizon. They are Pisces, whose one "fish" is just peaking above the horizon and Aquarius, which is also only partly visible between the bright star Altair and the horizon. Also between Altair and the southeastern horizon are the stars of Capricornus, the Horned Goat, a large constellation that stretches between Sagittarius and Aquarius.

PRACTISE YOUR SKILLS

(a) Finding the Bright Stars

The following 7 very bright stars are labelled on Map 4. They are very easy to find in a clear sky. Check them off when you have found them. (You may notice that now there are fewer very bright stars to see than at any other time of the year. The winter sky certainly contains more than the summer sky. Compare the number on this checklist with that for Map 2 and Map 6.)

- Polaris (the North Pole Star, brightest star in Ursa Minor)
- Arcturus (very bright, red giant star in Bootes)
- Vega (brightest star in Lyra)
- Spica (brightest star in Virgo)
- Antares (brightest star in Scorpius; very reddish-orange in colour)
- Altair (brightest star in Aquila; only about 16 light-years away)
- Deneb (brightest star in Cygnus; 100 times as far away as Altair)

(b) 6 Interesting Objects for Binoculars

These are among the best of the deep sky objects currently visible. You should try to observe them before going on to others.

- M6 and M7 (These two open clusters in Scorpius are low in the south, but are excellent objects. They are rich in bright stars.)
- M22 (This globular cluster near the "top of the teapot" in Sagittarius is a beautiful bright object in steadily held binoculars.)
- M8 (The famous Lagoon Nebula is just above the "spout of the teapot" in Sagittarius. It shows both nebulosity and a star cluster.)
- M4 (This bright globular cluster is easy to find beside the star Antares.)
- M11 (This is a bright open cluster of stars in Scutum. Notice its unusual shape.)

(c) Deep Sky Objects for the Small Telescope

The following is a checklist of the 27 Deep Sky Objects shown on Map 4. Each one is indicated by a tiny circle of dots.

> Before trying to observe the objects on this list, be sure to read the information above the list on pages 37-38.

- M6 (bright star cluster in Scorpius)
- M7 (star cluster in Scorpius, near M6, and bright enough to see naked eye) (Both of these clusters are quite low in the southern sky.)

- M22 (globular star cluster in Sagittarius)

- M8 (Lagoon Nebula in Sagittarius)

- M17 (Omega Nebula in Sagittarius)

- M11 (open star cluster in Scutum)

- M4 (globular star cluster in Scorpius, just to the right of Antares)

- M89, M84, M58 (three galaxies in the constellation Virgo)
  (The great cluster of galaxies found between the stars of Leo and Virgo is now low in the west and may be difficult to observe.)

- M5 (a globular star cluster in Serpens Caput)

- M13 (a bright globular cluster in Hercules, the one marked on the western side of this constellation)

- M92 (a globular cluster in Hercules, the one marked on the northern side of this constellation)
  (Hercules is now very high in the sky. This is a good time to view these two clusters.)

- M3 (a globular cluster in Canes Venatici)

- M27 (a planetary nebula in the constellation Vulpecula; found on the map above the "G" in the word "SAGITTA")

- M51 (the famous Whirlpool Galaxy in Canes Venatici; it is marked on the map just below the end star in the handle of the Big Dipper)

- M101 (a large "face-on" spiral galaxy in Ursa Major; marked above the end star in the handle of the Big Dipper)

- M106 (a galaxy in Canes Venatici; marked on the map half-way between the cup of the Big Dipper and the stars of Canes Venatici)

- M63 (a spiral galaxy in Canes Venatici; marked on the map above the first letter in the words "Canes Venatici")

- M81 (a spiral galaxy in Ursa Major; marked on the star map between the cup of the Big Dipper and the constellation Camelopardalis)

- M2 (a globular cluster in Aquarius; marked on the star map half-way between the words "Equuleus" and "Aquarius")

- M15 (a globular cluster in Pegasus; marked on the star map just above the word "Equuleus")

- M31 (the famous Andromeda Galaxy; marked on the star map just below the third letter in the word "Andromeda")

- M33 (the famous Pinwheel Galaxy in Triangulum; marked on the star map just below M31 and near the horizon)
  (Both of these galaxies are now very close to the northeastern horizon; it is wise to wait until later in the night to have a better view of them.)

- M39 (an open star cluster near Deneb in Cygnus)

- NGC869 (part of the Double Cluster, along with NGC884; also called "h and X Persei"; may be seen naked eye and found between the stars of Perseus and Cassiopeia)

- NGC6960 (part of the Veil Nebula, along with NGC6979; it is now high in the sky and just below the "left arm" of the Northern Cross in Cygnus)

The September-October Night Sky (Map 5)

Constellations and Naked-Eye Objects

For viewing the sky during the times given on Map 5, you may use the following as your guide.

You will notice that some of the constellations previously seen in the western sky and marked on Map 4 have now set below the western horizon. Certain other constellations, that you did not previously see, have now risen above the eastern horizon.

The constellations that are now no longer seen in the western sky are some of the late spring and summer constellations: Virgo, Libra, Scorpius, most of Sagittarius, and part of Bootes.

The constellations that have appeared in the east are Auriga, Aries, Taurus, and Cetus, and Piscis Austrinus which is in the south.

With some adjustment, you can use the description of the constellations for Map 4, if you remember that all of them have moved westward a certain amount.

The Constellations of the Northern Sky

Using the information you learned in Chapter 3, you will easily find the Big Dipper in the northern sky. The first thing that you will notice about it is that it is now low in the sky with the cup of the dipper very near the northern point of the horizon. After using the "Pointer Stars" to find Polaris, the North Pole Star, you will see that the Little Dipper in *Ursa Minor* stretches out toward the west and lies almost parallel to the northern horizon. The stars of *Draco*, the Dragon, extend to the westward between the two dippers, curl around the cup of the Little Dipper, and then extend again to the west where the head points to *Hercules* which is now low in the western sky. Tracing an imaginary line from the handle of the Big Dipper to Polaris and then extending it on an equal distance again brings us to the "W" of the constellation *Cassiopeia*, the Queen. This time we find that Cassiopeia is much higher in the sky, and it may now be easier to notice that it is inside the Milky Way, the great band of hazy brightness that extends across the dome of the sky. Slightly up and to the left from this star pattern is the "little house" of *Cepheus*, the King, with the "roof" of this five-star pattern pointing back down to Polaris as if the "house of Cepheus" is upside-down. Only part of Cepheus is within the Milky Way. The large area of sky extending down from Polaris to the northeastern horizon is occupied by the two "animal constellations", *Camelopardalis*, the Giraffe, and *Lynx*, the Lynx. None of their stars is very bright; you will be fortunate to see as many as are marked on the star map. In the northeast, Capella and the other bright stars of *Auriga* have risen enough to be easily seen, but further to the east, Aldebaran and a few of the stars of *Taurus* are so close to the horizon that they may not be noticed at all if there are trees or hills blocking the view. If it is possible to see bright, reddish Aldebaran and its companion stars in the Hyades cluster, you are catching a first glimpse of what the ancient peoples called the "rainy Hyades". When they saw them rising in the fall, they knew they should expect the rainy season of the year.

The Milky Way Crossing the Zenith As already observed, *Cassiopeia* and part of *Cepheus* are within the Milky Way and high in the sky. Following along this great wide pathway from Cassiopeia to Cepheus and continuing southwestward, you come to *Cygnus* or the Northern Cross, with its brightest star, Deneb, very close to the zenith. If observing conditions are good, it will be easy to see that the Milky Way extends completely across the heavens from northeast to southwest. Follow its wide path to the southwest from Cygnus. Notice the short arrow called *Sagitta*, below Albireo, the star at the foot of the Northern Cross. Below it you will see *Aquila*, the Eagle, with the bright and relatively close star, Altair, the southernmost member of the Summer Triangle. Still further below it, you will see *Scutum*, the Shield, and the star clouds in and below this constellation.

The Summer Stars in the Western and Southwestern Sky The Summer Triangle of stars, Deneb, Vega, and Altair, are now well to the west of the zenith. Libra, Scorpius, and most of Sagittarius — the constellations that dominated the southern sky during the nights of summer — have now sunk below the western horizon. Only the handle of the "teapot of *Sagittarius*" remains visible in the southwest. Only parts of *Ophiuchus* and *Serpens* are above the west-southwestern horizon. *Hercules* is low in west, and below him, *Corona Borealis*, the Northern Crown, which will be difficult to see if there are trees or other obstructions near the western horizon.

Autumn's "Watery" Constellations in the South and Southeast As mentioned above, the ancient peoples knew the autumn as the rainy season. It is little wonder that the star patterns of this time of year are sometimes called the "watery constellations". In the southern and southeastern sky six creatures bear this association. Eastward from Altair is the small constellation named *Delphinus*, the Dolphin, which many observers claim actually looks like a dolphin leaping out of the sea. Southward from Altair is the constellation *Capricornus*, the Sea Goat or the Horned Goat. To the east of it is the large sprawling constellation *Aquarius*, the Water-bearer. Below Aquarius and low in the south is *Piscis Austrinus*, the Southern Fish, a small constellation of relatively faint stars except for one bright one named Fomalhaut. From our northern latitudes, this star is above the southern horizon for only a short while each year, but it is bright enough to be easily detected.

If you look from the zenith down toward the eastern horizon, you will notice first the Great Square of Pegasus and extending off to the left from it the three bright stars and other fainter ones in the constellation Andromeda. Below them are the final two "watery constellations", *Pisces*, the Fish, and *Cetus*, the Sea Monster or Whale. Pisces has no stars as bright as the Summer Triangle. Careful observation will reveal a string of stars forming a large letter "V" pointing down to the horizon. The top ends of the "V" show two circles of stars, one below the Square of Pegasus and one below Andromeda. Cetus appears as a strange configuration of stars, some of them brighter than any in Pisces. Stretched along the eastern horizon, as the map indicates, Cetus has two patterns of four or five stars joined by a string of fainter stars. One of the stars in that string is the famous variable called Mira, the "Wonderful Star", one of the first stars noted to be variable. In fact, its variation in brightness is so great that at times it is as bright as the stars in the Square of Pegasus and at other times it is barely seen in ordinary binoculars. It is certainly one of the most interesting objects in the constellation Cetus.

PRACTISE YOUR SKILLS

(a) Finding the Bright Stars

Check off the following 9 named stars when you observe them.

- Polaris (the North Pole Star, brightest star in Ursa Minor)
- Aldebaran (the "eye of the bull" in Taurus)
- Algol (famous variable star with a regular period of about 2.9 days)
- Mira (famous variable star in Cetus; varies widely in brightness)
- Fomalhaut (brightest star in Piscis Austrinus; always seen in the far southern sky from our northern latitudes)
- Altair (brightest star in Aquila)
- Deneb (brightest star in Cygnus)
- Capella ("the Goat Star", brightest in Auriga)
- Vega (brightest star in Lyra)

(b) 4 Interesting Objects for Binoculars

The following are among the most interesting objects to be seen at this time of year. Check them on this list, after observing them in binoculars.

- M15 (This bright globular cluster in Pegasus is easily seen in binoculars.)
- M11 (This open cluster in Scutum is a beautiful sight in binoculars. Note the pattern of the 4 stars beside it.)
- M31 (Steadily held binoculars will reveal some of the structure in this great galaxy in Andromeda.)
- M33 (This galaxy is not as bright as M31, but its large size always surprises beginning observers. It is in Triangulum.)

(c) Deep Sky Objects for the Small Telescope

There are 19 Deep Sky Objects shown on Map 5. The first 15 of them were more fully described on the checklist for Map 4 (pages 58-60).

> Before observing the objects on this list, be sure to read the information above the checklist on pages 37-38.

- M2 (globular star cluster in constellation Aquarius)
- M15 (globular star cluster in constellation Pegasus)
- M11 (open star cluster in constellation Scutum)
- M27 (planetary nebula in constellation Vulpecula)
- M13 (globular star cluster in constellation Hercules)
- M92 (globular star cluster in constellation Hercules)
- M101 (spiral galaxy in constellation Ursa Major)
- M51 (spiral galaxy in constellation Canes Venatici)
- M106 (galaxy in constellation Canes Venatici)
- M81 (spiral galaxy in constellation Ursa Major)
- M31 (famous naked-eye spiral galaxy in constellation Andromeda)
- M33 (spiral galaxy in constellation Triangulum)
- M39 (open star cluster in constellation Cygnus)
- NGC869 (part of double star cluster in constellation Perseus)

- NGC6960 (part of the Veil Nebula in constellation Cygnus)
- M36 (open cluster in constellation Auriga)
- M37 (open cluster in constellation Auriga)
- M38 (open cluster in constellation Auriga)
  (As the star map shows, these three clusters are very low near the northeastern horizon. Wait until later for a better view of them.)
- M45 (This is the Pleiades Star Cluster. It has just risen above the eastern horizon and will be easy to observe over the coming months.)

The November-December Night Sky (Map 6)

Constellations and Naked-Eye Objects

For viewing the sky during the times given on Map 6, you may use the following as your guide.

You will notice that some of the constellations previously seen in the western sky and marked on Map 5 have now set below the western horizon. Certain other constellations, that you did not previously see, have now risen above the eastern horizon.

The constellations that are now no longer seen in the western sky are the "late summer constellations": Ophiuchus and Serpens, Corona Borealis, Hercules, Scutum, Capricornus, and most of Aquila.

The constellations that have appeared in the east are the "early winter constellations": Gemini, Orion, Monoceros, Canis Minor, Lepus, and Eridanus.

With some adjustment, you can use the description of the constellations for Maps 4 and 5, if you remember that all of them have moved westward.

The Constellations of the Northern Sky

From the information learned in Chapter 3, you will find that the Big Dipper in *Ursa Major* is very low near the northern horizon. In fact, the end of the handle is almost touching the horizon. After using the "Pointer Stars" in the cup of the dipper to point to Polaris, the North Pole Star, you will notice that the Little Dipper seems to be hanging on a hook in the sky. The cup of this dipper is almost directly below Polaris. *Draco* curls down toward the northwestern horizon, apparently searching for Hercules who has now disappeared from the sky. Tracing an imaginary line up from the Big Dipper's handle to Polaris and on toward the zenith brings you to the constellation *Cassiopeia*, the Queen, whose bright stars now look more like the letter "M" than a "W" to those who have been facing north. King *Cepheus* is now found below Cassiopeia and above Draco. To the eastward from Polaris, the zoo animals, *Camelopardalis*, the Giraffe, and *Lynx*, the Lynx, sprawl across a large area of sky with few bright stars until you notice the bright "twin stars", Castor and Pollux, that have now risen in the east.

The Summer Triangle Low in the West After dominating the sky for over six months, the Summer Triangle of stars, Altair in Aquila, Deneb in Cygnus, and Vega in Lyra, are now ready to set in the west. Notice that

now the Northern Cross, with Deneb at the top of it, is standing upright above the west-northwestern horizon. Altair and Vega are very low and may not be seen if trees or other obstacles interfere.

The Milky Way Stretching from East to West If observing conditions are good, you will notice that the Milky Way forms a great pathway across the sky from east to west. The rich star clouds of the Summer Milky Way have disappeared in the west. The less distinct Winter Milky Way is just rising in the east. Try to observe it carefully to notice where it widens and narrows as it crosses the sky.

The "Watery" Constellations Filling the Southern Sky Most of the star patterns in the southern half of the sky are the "watery" constellations seen on Map 5, with the addition of another member of the same group. To view all seven of them we can start with the Great Square of Pegasus, which is now west of the zenith. Between it and the western horizon is *Delphinus*, the Dolphin, which now seems to be rising out of a body of water on the western horizon. Equuleus, the Colt, is now scarcely noticeable since its few faint stars are so close to the horizon. Moving from the Great Square to the southwest brings you to *Aquarius*, the Water-bearer and *Piscis Austrinus*, the Southern Fish, whose bright star, Fomalhaut, is barely above the horizon. Only a few stars of *Capricornus*, the Sea Goat or the Horned Goat, are still above the horizon; Star Map 6 shows only two of them. The southern point of the Great Square directs the way to Pisces, just as the "V" of *Pisces* directs the way to *Cetus*, the Sea Monster or Whale and the great river of stars called *Eridanus*. This large region of the sky contains many stars that are visible on a clear night but scarcely any that are very bright as viewed from our northern latitudes. (However, one star of Eridanus, seen only in southern latitudes, is among the brightest stars in the sky; it is known as Achernar and is found at the far southern end of the great river.) The upper end of the river seems to flow toward Rigel, the brightest star in Orion. The appearance of Orion is the signal that the stars of winter are about to make their appearance.

The Bright Stars of Winter Rising in the East From overhead where Cassiopeia and Perseus lie within the stars of the Milky Way, you should direct your attention eastward where many bright stars of winter are rising. Moving straight east from the curving row of stars in Perseus you come to the five bright stars of Auriga, the Charioteer, known for its collection of star clusters. Below it the constellation Gemini, the Twins, has risen, with Castor and Pollux shining brightly on the northern side of the constellation. Below them Cancer, the Crab, is peeking above the horizon, and Procyon, the brightest star in Canis Minor, the Small Dog, is also visible in a due easterly direction. South of Auriga, the head of Taurus, the Bull, is easily seen because of the bright reddish star, Aldebaran. Above it riding on the back of the bull are the Pleiades, or Seven Sisters, a famous star cluster that is one of the brightest in the sky. Below Taurus, Orion, the Hunter, is making his appearance. He now seems to be lying on his back, but he will later stand upright and march across the sky. One of the most distinctive constellations of all, Orion has many bright stars, only two of which, Rigel and Betelgeuse, are labelled on the star map. To the south of the Hunter is Lepus the rabbit, just above the horizon and appearing to accompany him across the sky. Keen sky watchers are always excited by the rising of Orion and his accompanying constellations; they bring a promise of many interesting objects to be seen in the winter skies.

PRACTISE YOUR SKILLS

(a) Finding the Bright Stars

The following 14 bright stars are labelled on Map 6. They are very easy to find in a clear sky. Check off each one when you identify it. (Compare the number of bright stars at this time of year with the number you saw during the summer when using Map 4.)

- Polaris (the North Pole Star, brightest star in Ursa Minor)
- Aldebaran (the "eye of the bull" in Taurus)
- Algol (variable star with a regular period of about 2.9 days)
- Mira (variable star in Cetus; known for its remarkable variation)
- Fomalhaut (brightest star in Piscis Austrinus; always seen in the far southern sky from our northern latitudes)
- Altair (brightest star in Aquila)
- Deneb (brightest star in Cygnus)
- Capella ("the Goat Star", brightest in Auriga)
- Vega (brightest star in Lyra)
- Castor and Pollux (the Twin Stars in Gemini)
- Procyon (the Little Dog Star in Canis Minor)
- Betelgeuse (the slightly variable red giant star in Orion)
- Rigel (the very bright "knee of Orion")

(b) 7 Interesting Objects for Binoculars

The following 7 are among the best of the deep sky objects to try to observe this time of year. Be sure to observe them before going to other objects.

- M31 (The Andromeda Galaxy is now high in the sky. With steady binoculars, its shape as a spiral galaxy is clearly seen.)

- M33 (If conditions are very good, you should try to find the famous Pinwheel Galaxy not far from M31 and also a member of the Local Group of Galaxies.
  It is very large and "face-on", but not as bright as M31. Binoculars are better than a telescope for finding it.)

- M36, M37, AND M38 (Since the constellation Auriga is now high in the eastern sky, it is the ideal time to find these three open clusters, almost in a row, and in the central part of the constellation. Try to notice slight differences in the three of them.)

- M45 (The famous Pleiades Cluster is a delight in good binoculars. If conditions are good, challenge yourself to see some of the nebulosity near several of the brightest stars.)

- NGC869 (The Double Cluster between the stars of Cassiopeia and Perseus is now near the zenith. It is a dazzling sight in binoculars.)

(c) Deep Sky Objects for the Small Telescope

There are 19 Deep Sky Objects shown on Map 6. The first 15 of them were described on the checklists for Map 4 and Map 5.

> Before trying to observe the objects on this list, be sure to read the information above the list on pages 37-38.

- M2 (globular star cluster in constellation Aquarius)

- M15 (globular star cluster in constellation Pegasus)

- M27 (planetary nebula in constellation Vulpecula)

- M101 (spiral galaxy in constellation Ursa Major)

- M51 (spiral galaxy in constellation Canes Venatici)

- M36 (open star cluster in constellation Auriga)

- M37 (open star cluster in constellation Auriga)

- M38 (open star cluster in constellation Auriga)

- M45 (famous Pleiades star cluster in constellation Taurus)
- M31 (naked-eye spiral galaxy in constellation Andromeda)
- M33 (large spiral galaxy in constellation Triangulum)
- M39 (open star cluster in constellation Cygnus)
- M81 (spiral galaxy in constellation Ursa Major)
- NGC869 (part of the double star cluster in Perseus)
- NGC6960 (part of the Veil Nebula in Cygnus)
- M1 (the Crab Nebula, a supernova remnant; marked on the map near the star that forms the "end of the horn" of Taurus)
- M35 (an open cluster in Gemini; marked on the map near the stars that form the "foot of Castor")
- M42 (the large, beautiful Orion Nebula, an emission nebula; marked on the map as part of the "sword of Orion")
- M44 (the Beehive Cluster, an open cluster in Cancer; marked on the map just below the second "C" in the word "Cancer")

Chapter 7

Tips on Becoming a Better Observer

If you want to become a better-than-average observer, you should listen to the advice of many very experienced observers who are recognized as being good amateur astronomers. They will usually share with you important information about how to improve your skills and take advantage of the time you spend under the night sky.

Here are some of the tips that many skilled observers follow whenever they observe the night sky.

1. Before each observing session there are some important questions to be asked:

What time of night will I be observing?

Will the moon be in the sky during that time of night?

If so, will the moon rise or set during that time?

If the moon will be up, will it be bright enough to interfere
with what I want to observe?

Depending on whether the moon rises or sets, and when it rises or sets,
you may be able to plan when you can observe certain objects, either
before it rises or after it sets, if the objects are too faint to be easily seen
while the moon is in the sky. See the chapter about the moon to find
out *approximately* when the moon will be rising or setting on a
particular night.

2.   Be sure to study a map of the constellations that will be up in the sky
     while you will be observing. Begin with the appropriate map from this
     guide. From this constellation map, and perhaps some other star
     maps, if you have them, you can plan what you want to observe.

3.   Make a list of the lunar features (if you are going to observe the moon),
     the planets, stars and other objects that you want to observe. Leave a
     space after each one so that you can check them off when you observe
     them, and so that you can add a few comments about the appearance
     of each one or anything unusual about the appearance of each one.
     Take this list on a clipboard or in a notepad along with you to your
     observing site. Do not forget also to take a pen that has black ink or
     ink of a dark colour, certainly not red, since writing in red ink
     disappears under the light of a red flashlight which you will probably
     be using.

4.   When you get ready to go out to observe, remember the following:

     (1)   Avoid looking at bright lights for about a 1/2 hour before going
           out.

     (2)   "Dark adapt" before going outdoors. This means that you should
           give your eyes a chance to become accustomed to the darkness.
           If possible turn off most or all of the lights in the room while you
           are preparing, so that you will not have to spend as long later
           becoming able to see faint objects. It takes the human eye about
           15 minutes to become well enough accustomed to the dark to see
           objects as faint as most amateur astronomers want to see.

     (3)   Dress warmly, especially if the weather is cold. It is extremely
           important to cover the head well, even if you feel there is no
           danger of frozen ears. Do not take chances with the cold. Many

experienced observers use winter clothes even in the summer. If you become warm, they can always be removed, as they should be, so that you avoid sweating. Dress "in layers". On a spring or summer evening, it is better to have two or three warm sweaters available than one heavy coat. The sweaters can be put on as the need arises.

(4) Take with you a dim, *red-light* flashlight to read your star maps — not a white-light flashlight. White light destroys the dark adaption that your eyes have acquired, and if you look at a white-light flashlight, it will be about 15 minutes more before you will again be able to see faint objects effectively. You do not need to buy an expensive red-light flashlight, if you do not have one. Simply convert the one you have. Either remove the bulb, paint it with a dark red paint or nail polish, and reinsert it, or cover the front of your regular flashlight with heavy red or brown paper.

When you are at your observing site, remember the following:

(1) Move slowly and cautiously when you are near tripod-mounted binoculars or a telescope. Sudden movements in the dark can cause you to hit an instrument and even damage it.

(2) When using hand-held binoculars always use the neck strap, for safety, to avoid dropping them. Move them slowly from one position to another. If the binoculars are mounted on a tripod, move the binoculars slowly and carefully and lock them securely in the required position before studying the object you want to observe. Sometimes when beginners are hand-holding their binoculars, they hold them too close to the eye-piece end of the instrument. Try to find the balance point of the binoculars and hold them at that point. You will see that it is closer to the "big end" than the "small end". This may seem like a small matter, but after a while you will find that it is much less tiring to do it this way, and you will be able to observe much longer and without having sore arms.

(3) Do not rush quickly from one object to another. Take your time to enjoy the view, and to appreciate and study each object.

(4) Check off each item on the list you prepared before the observing session. Add notes and make drawings showing what you are observing. Challenge yourself: in your drawings, try to show as much detail as you possibly can, even if it is a fairly faint object.

(5) If you are observing with tripod-mounted binoculars or a telescope, take a deep breath in order to relax and concentrate

before looking at a faint or difficult object. While you are observing, try not to breathe on the binoculars or the eyepiece if you are observing with a telescope. Your breath could cause condensation which is often called "dewing" or "fogging" on the lens or eyepiece, or even "frosting" if the weather is cold. If "dewing" or "frosting" does happen, you should *not* take the instrument indoors immediately. That would only make the condition worse; instead, you should use a hair dryer carefully to circulate warm air over the surface where the condensation or frost is on the instrument.

(6) Find a location where there are no street lights or other outdoor lights glaring into your eyes. If you are observing from your backyard, find the spot that is the darkest.

(7) If the weather is very cold, go indoors every half hour to get warm. To avoid having to spend a while "dark adapting" all over again, have the indoor lights dimmed or turned out, if possible, when you go inside to get warm.

5. After the observing session is over, record your observations in your log or observing notebook as soon as possible. Use the checklist you prepared earlier and the notes and drawings you made while observing. Refer to the next chapter, Recording Observations, for one easy way of doing it.

Chapter 8

Recording Observations

Why Record Observations?

Have you ever seen a bright meteor? Or a beautiful sunset? Or a display of the Northern Lights? You have? Really? When?

If you did not record somewhere these marvelous events, then, in a way, you have lost part of them. You might be able to describe the sudden flash and the long train of the meteor, or the lovely stratus clouds that accompanied the sunset, but what happens later on when you see another meteor or sunset and you try to compare the new sighting with the old one?

Or what happens, if a friend tells you about a fabulous meteor or sunset that he or she saw two weeks ago and you do no know if the one you saw was on the same date as your friend's. You cannot find out because you did not record it.

There is another reason for recording your observations. Since you may often share your work with other people, you need to get the details straight so that they will understand clearly the beauty of what you saw, and they can compare it with what they have seen or did not see.

Besides, recording your observations is fun — to write, and to read later, perhaps many years later. A diary of your observing memories can last a lifetime, perhaps several lifetimes. Modern amateur astronomers find it very interesting to read the observing log kept by Charles Messier over two hundred years ago. He was a comet hunter who wrote such careful and exact notes that we can easily imagine what his observing sessions were like.

A Simple Method of Recording Observations

Exactly what type of records you keep is entirely up to you. Some observers like to use a simple notebook in which they write all notes and do all drawings one after the other. Other people, like me, like to use a science or laboratory type of notebook in which the left-hand page is blank and the right-hand page is lined, so that they can do their drawings and sketches on the left side, and write their notes on the right side. Whichever you choose is up to you, but you should have a notebook of some sort, get a new one when it is filled, and keep all your old ones in order in a safe place.

When I write my notes on the right-hand pages in my observing notebook, I use a simple code that I devised many years ago. Inventing a code for yourself, or borrowing one that someone else uses, can be very helpful. In that way you do not have to use many words over and over, because certain words *are* used very frequently.

The first thing you may want to write is a number of the observing session. Some observers have numbers that are up in the thousands, because they started keeping an observing notebook or log when they were quite young and first started observing things in the sky.

Next, many observers write a letter for the time of day or night of the observing session. The letters that can be used are: *e, n, m,* and *d,* standing for evening, night, morning, and daytime (since some astronomers do observe things in the sky in the daytime).

Most good observing logs contain five pieces of information about the observing session, often in code so that they appear on one line at the beginning of the entry: (1) date, (2) time, (3) location, (4) sky conditions, and (5) instrument used.

Concerning the *date*, if it is a night-time observing session, you should use a "double-date" because the date, as you know, changes at midnight. This is followed by the *start and end times* of the observing session. The *location* should be named unless all observing in the whole log is done from the same place.

Regarding *sky conditions*, some observers use a ten-point descriptive code. Such a scale may be used under both city and rural conditions. The range goes from very poor to very good. The number *0* means almost totally overcast or almost no sky visible. *1, 2,* and *3* refer respectively to a very cloudy, mainly cloudy, and partly cloudy sky. The digits 4 through 7 may apply to backyard observing from a city-bound site: very hazy or murky (*4*), hazy or murky (*5*), slightly hazy or murky (*6*), and acceptably clear (*7*). Under dark rural or country conditions, a person may use the numbers *8* through *10*: for a quite clear sky (*8*), a very clear sky (*9*), or an absolutely fantastic sky (*10*).

Then, you should indicate *how* you are observing, that is, whether it is with the unaided eye ("ne" for "naked eye"), or with binoculars ("b"), or with a telescope ("t"), in which case you should name the type of telescope or size and eyepiece used. All of this information can be given in one line *in coded form* and can be recorded in a few seconds after you become used to doing it.

Then, you should record the names of others who observed with you (if there was anyone with you). Finally and most important of all, you need to list the *objects* you observed or type of observation you did.

Here is an example of the recording of an observing session:

140n 1993, Jan.20-21 22:30-23:50EST backyard 7 ne & 10x50b Fred & Jane

ne: – winter constellations
       – very bright meteor at 22:46, a bit brighter than Sirius
         going from the belt of Orion south past Lepus to
         Columba

10x50b: – the Pleiades – beautiful (!)
        – Orion nebula – very nice
        – two clusters of stars in Auriga (M37 and M38)

In this entry from a "make-believe" observing log, the person was describing observing session number 140, which was on the night of January 20, 1993. The "double date" was used to avoid confusion caused by the change of date at midnight. The session began at 10:30 p.m. and ended at 11:50 p.m., just ten minutes before midnight. The writer used the 24-hour clock system. The letters "EST" indicates that it was Eastern Standard Time. There could be some confusion if the time system were not mentioned, especially during the summer months when Daylight Saving Time is used. The person was observing from his/her backyard. The only instrument was a pair of 10x50 binoculars and he/she was observing with friends, Fred and Jane. The wonderful meteor that they saw was recorded, and now it will not be forgotten because the observer took two minutes to write it down.

A More Advanced Method of Recording Observations

As you observe more and more objects, you will have an even greater need to record them, and so you will develop a more complete code for information that you want to write down. It may be helpful for you to write down in the back of your notebook the explanation for your code as it grows.

Here are some samples of a code that you may develop for places where you do your observations:

by	– my own *backyard*
Fob	– my friend, *F*red's *ob*servatory
yc	– the *y*ard at our summer *c*ottage
lc	– the shore along the *l*ake at our summer *c*ottage
dn	– the *d*eck on the *n*orth side of our cottage.

As you include other items in the code for sky conditions, you may expand that one to include such things as the following:

10.5	– more than superb conditions (!), the best I have ever seen in my life (This may have been from a place high in the mountains or very far from any city.)
cml	– *c*rescent *m*oon*l*ight
gml	– *g*ibbous *m*oon*l*ight
fml	– *f*ull *m*oon*l*ight.
	(Moonlight conditions prevent an observer from seeing many stars and other objects that might otherwise be seen.)

Advanced observers should record the type of instruments they use, and may wish to use the following code:

11x80b – binoculars of 11 power with lenses of 80 mm diameter
20cmrt – a reflecting type of telescope with a mirror of 20cm diameter
10cmra – a refractor (lens) type of telescope with a lens of 10cm diameter
20cmsct – a Schmidt-Cassegrain type of telescope with a 20cm aperture

The eyepiece or ocular used in the telescope should be listed also. For example:

28m-o – with a 28mm eyepiece or ocular
19m-o – with a 19mm eyepiece or ocular

Here is a sample section from the observing log of another observer:

982n 1993, May 24-25 23:20-02:20EST yc 9.5 ne & 10x50b & 20cmrt, 32m-o _____

ne: – 20 constellations
         – meteor at 23:56EST as bright as Spica → SW from Lyr to Boo
10X35b: – M6 OC in Sco, M7 OC in Sco.
20cmrt: – Beta Cyg DS, M22 GC in Sag (!), M65 SG in Leo.

You can see that this person was observing alone for three hours in the yard at the summer cottage under superb conditions and using a 20cm relecting telescope with a 32mm ocular. Besides seeing many constellations, this person observed a bright meteor with the unaided eye and two objects with his binoculars, as well as three objects with the telescope. The meteor was as bright as the brightest star in the constellation Virgo and it *was moving* (→) *southwestward (SW)* from the constellation Lyra to the constellation Bootes. The objects observed with the binoculars were two large *open clusters (OC)* of stars (M6 and M7) in the constellations Scorpius. The objects observed with the telescope were the famous *double star (DS)* – Beta in the constellation Cygnus, M22 – a *globular cluster (GC)* in the constellation Sagittarius, and finally M65 – a *spiral galaxy (SG)* in the constellation Leo.

The exclamation mark after M22 indicates that the observer thought that it was a fabulous view of this object, perhaps the best view that this person had ever seen of this star cluster. If the observer wanted to, he or she could also have written other personal notes about this object or others.

As observers become more skilled year after year, they usually continue to invent even more advanced codes to describe more completely the sky conditions (naming both the transparency and the "seeing", or lack of turbulence in the atmosphere) and to state more the details about the appearance of the objects observed, whether they are planets, galaxies, star clusters, or comets.

By using simple codes such as these, a great deal of information can be recorded in your observing log in a very short while, and it can be very useful to you later.

Chapter 9

The Importance of Binoculars

The human eye is the greatest optical instrument in the world. Far too many beginning observers think that they need expensive equipment to observe the night sky and to appreciate its many wonders. They fail to realize that there are many things that can be seen as well or better without any equipment at all. Meteor showers and displays of the aurora are good examples of what is best observed with the unaided eye.

Many beginning observers also think that they need an expensive telescope to observe many distant objects in the sky, and they fail to realize that hundreds of objects can be observed just as well *or better* with binoculars than with a telescope.

There are many advantages to owning a pair of binoculars. Binoculars are versatile instruments. Many models may be used at sporting events or when one is vacationing or sight-seeing. In fact, some people may find that they already have a pair that was once used at spectator sporting events, and is quite suitable for enjoying views of the night sky.

Binoculars are sometimes the best possible instrument for viewing certain objects such as large star clusters like the Pleiades or the Hyades, for locating many objects especially if the area of the sky is not well-known, for finding the planets Uranus and Neptune which cannot be seen with the unaided eye, for locating the brighter planets in twilight, and for studying bright comets or the moon during a lunar eclipse.

Binoculars allow the observer to use both eyes — a definite advantage over telescopes. When using both eyes you can relax in a way that is not possible when using only one eye. The two eyes can assist and complement each other. Faint objects will appear brighter than they will in a telescope, and the viewer can have a better sense of the realism of the object being viewed.

When choosing a pair of binoculars, one should keep a few things in mind. Most binoculars are designated by two numbers with an "X" between them. The first number indicates the magnification or the "power" that they give you. Objects in "7 power" binoculars appear seven times closer or larger than they do to the unaided eye. The second number tells you the diameter in millimetres of the main or larger lens. The larger the diameter of the lenses, the greater ability they have to gather light. This "light gathering ability" is very important for all binoculars and telescopes. The more light they can gather, the brighter the objects will appear. The first number, the magnification, is important, also, but perhaps not as important as most people think. You must remember that the *higher* the magnification, the *smaller* the "field of view" or area of the sky that you will see. There is not much point in having high magnification, if you can not find most of the things that you want to view, or have to spend most of your time searching for objects and then, after you find them, discover that that you can see only a small part of the object because it is too big to fit into the field of your binoculars. Binoculars with high power are also extremely difficult to hand-hold. The objects that you want to see appear to "jump all over".

What binoculars are best for observing objects in the night sky? 7X50 or 10X50 binoculars give a wide field and generally give bright images. 8X40s are also good. These three are well suited to astronomy, as well as being suitable for other purposes. "Zoom" binoculars, that is, those with variable magnification, such as 7-15X35, are *not* recommended; they are often poor quality instruments.

Should binoculars be mounted on a tripod? It is recommended that a tripod be used with binoculars over 7X, if you are using them for longer than just a few minutes. A tripod steadies the images and makes studying them much easier. Some binoculars have tripod adapters already on them; others do not. If your binoculars do not have a tripod adapter, you may buy one at a camera store. A good sturdy tripod is well worth the investment. It makes your binocular observing sessions much more enjoyable. A tripod is an absolute necessity if you have large astronomical binoculars, such as 11X80 instruments.

When thinking about buying good quality binoculars, you should expect to pay from $50 or $60 to several hundred dollars depending on the size of the instrument. It is often said that price is a good indicator of quality when comparing instruments of the same size. Paying a slightly higher price will often mean obtaining instruments that have good quality optics and sturdy construction.

Owning and using a pair of good quality binoculars is suggested as a major step toward a lifetime of enjoying the views of the night sky.

Chapter 10

When to Buy a Telescope

Most beginning astronomers do not need a telescope as soon as they think they do, and too many beginners buy a telescope before they are prepared to use one properly. Sometimes, because they are not yet really prepared to use one, they become frustrated when it does not magically perform for them. Then they put it aside, and eventually lose interest. They lose out on a chance to view hundreds of wonderful objects in the sky.

The major reasons that beginners are unprepared to use a telescope are that they are not yet totally familiar with the sky, they do not yet know what objects in the sky are best viewed in a specific type of telescope, and they do not realize that most telescopes allow them to view only a very small piece of the sky at once. Some beginners also expect that, with a small telescope, they will see objects in exactly the same way as those objects have been photographed by the largest telescopes in the world and pictured in textbooks or magazines.

Before buying any telescope, a person should become familiar with the sky, should learn about what can be seen in certain areas of the sky and during certain seasons of the year, and should find as many objects as possible with a pair of binoculars. This means that you should study star maps, learn all the constellations that can be seen at a certain time, and try to identify as many of the very bright stars as possible. It also means that you should be able to identify the bright planets that can be seen at certain times.

Then you will be able to use *binoculars* to view more challenging things. You will be able to use them to search for the star clusters marked on the star maps in this book, such as the three that are found in the constellation Auriga. You will use them to view M31, the spiral galaxy in the constellation Andromeda. You will be able to find the globular cluster M13 in the constellation Hercules. You will be able to find the huge nebula of hydrogen gas called M42 in the sword of Orion, the great winter constellation in the southern sky.

Only then, *after* you have been able to identify these things and find them *both* with the unaided eye *and* with binoculars, should you consider buying a telescope. Even then, buying a telescope should not be a hasty decision. Perhaps it would be best to join an astronomy club, such as a Centre of the R.A.S.C. (See Chapter 19.) In the club you will meet people who own and use many kinds of telescopes. They can give you advice on the best type of telescope for your needs.

There are several things that always need to be considered when a person thinks he or she is ready to purchase a telescope. They can be listed as follows:

(a) *PORTABILITY* There is no need to buy a huge telescope if you live in an apartment and need to travel for an hour every time you set it up and use it. It is better to own a small, very portable telescope that could be used every clear night, rather than a huge one that would be used only once a month.

(b) *EASE OF USE* A simple telescope for beginners is better than one with advanced features that would require a long time to learn about. There is a place for complicated and sophisticated technology, but a beginner needs to concentrate on finding objects in the sky, not to be spending precious time, particularly on cold winter nights, leaning how to operate certain unnecessary options on an untested telescope.

(c) *PRICE* The cost, or initial investment, is an important consideration for most people. That is why this chapter began with the warning that too many people buy telescopes too soon in the course of their venture into astronomy. A good quality telescope is an *important* investment; a good quality telescope, properly used and maintained, should last a lifetime, yes, for forty or fifty years. Many telescopes that are much older than that are still being used, and their owners would never want to get rid of them.

There is a real danger that a beginner will spend money on a very poor quality "department store" telescope, one that will prove quite unsatisfactory. Then the money spent will be wasted, if the telescope is set aside and never used again. Most telescopes sold in department stores for $400. or less are not worth bringing home. On the other hand, some second-hand telescopes, available from members of astronomy clubs, because the original owner simply wanted to move on to a different type of telescope, are real bargains and may be exactly what a beginner should buy *if* he or she is ready to own a telescope. Such a telescope may be available for the same amount, or even less than a person would spent in a department store for a telescope that would prove almost worthless.

(d) *SUITABILITY FOR YOUR KIND OF OBSERVING* Certain types of telescopes are more suitable for some kinds of observing than others. A 100mm refractor may be very suitable for observing lunar craters and bright planets, but would not be a good telescope for observing faint galaxies. A fairly large reflector might be very good for observing faint galaxies but might not be a good telescope for observing detail on the surface of the planets. There are other considerations about the suitability of telescopes that you can learn from consulting with experienced telescope users.

Indeed, there are many considerations to take into account. The best advice is to consult with experienced observers, and consider your purchase and your needs very carefully.

In summary, you should probably purchase a telescope *only after* you have passed certain steps on the the road to becoming familiar with the sky, and with binocular observing. To find out whether you are ready for such a step, you can ask yourself the following eight questions:

1. Can I name four circumpolar constellations? (These are constellations in the northern sky that never set from locations in the earth's northern hemisphere. They appear on all the star maps in this book.)

2. Can I name three constellations that are seen in the southern sky in each of the four seasons of the year?

3. Can I name or explain the location of each of the following:
    (a) 4 double stars,
    (b) 4 variable stars,
    (c) 5 star clusters,
    (d) 5 nebulae or galaxies?

4. Have I seen all of the above objects (in # 3), either with the unaided eye or with binoculars?

5. Can I find all of the above objects by myself (using binoculars, if necessary)?

6.   Have I found all the bright stars on the maps in this book *and* the binocular objects listed for each star map? (This means you will have spent at least a year studying the sky with the unaided eye and with binoculars.)

7.   Am I familiar with the use of at least one star atlas in addition to the maps in this observing guide?

8.   Am I sure that I want to spend time learning how to operate a telescope in order that I may observe hundreds of fainter and more challenging objects?

If you can answer "Yes!" to *all seven* of these questions, then you may indeed be ready to own a telescope.

Do not be too hasty in making a purchase. Talk to several owners of different types of telescopes. Decide what is best for you and your circumstances. Be prepared to take the time to learn how to operate it properly. Your long-term rewards over future years of observing will probably be determined by whether you take the time to make the right decisions *before* purchasing your telescope.

Chapter 11

Observing the Moon

Everyone has observed the moon and been fascinated by it at one time or another. Not everyone, however, knows in advance what to expect from the moon on a certain night when he or she might wish to go out and observe what is in the night sky.

Will the moon be visible in the sky tonight? Will it be rising, or setting, or high in the sky when I want to observe? Will it be so bright or so close to an object that I want to observe that it will interfere with my seeing that object? After reading this chapter carefully you should easily be able to answer all of those questions.

What should I expect from the moon tonight? To answer that question, you always need to know what time it is *in the moon's cycle* or where the moon is in its monthly orbit around the earth. Our word "month" comes from the word "moon". Long ago our ancestors learned to measure the moon's cycle very accurately, and they found out that it was about 29 1/2 days between times when the moon was at the same phase. For example, it was 29 1/2 days between two new moons or two full moons. We all know from looking at calendars that there are four major phases listed: New Moon, First Quarter, Full Moon, and Last Quarter, and then the cycle repeats itself. The time of New Moon is really the beginning of the "lunar month". That is why we say that a moon that is only 2 days old is a "very young moon", and one that is 28 days old is a "very old moon". A moon's life cycle is only 29 1/2 days! Then a new life cycle begins. We can also see why the time between each one of the four major phases is about one week. Since the four major phases occur when the moon is at the beginning and is about 1/4, 1/2, and 3/4 through its life cycle, the time between each major phase is about 1/4 of 29 1/2 days or a little more than seven days.

In order to know what we should expect from the moon at any one time, we should ask what phase of the moon occurs today? Or, between which phases are we now?

Depending on the answer, we should follow these guidelines in order to know approximately what to expect from the moon.

Between the Time of New Moon and First Quarter

On the day of New Moon, the moon will appear too close to the sun to be seen at all.

During the week following New Moon, the moon will become visible in the evening in the western or southwestern sky. This will happen a half hour to an hour or more after sunset as the sky gets darker. One, two, or three days after New Moon, it will be a small crescent, gradually growing in size as the days go by. It is called a "waxing crescent moon". ("Waxing" means "growing".) The "horns of the crescent" will point away from the sun and upward or toward the south or southeast — toward the observer's left. As the crescent grows in size from night to night, it will appear brighter and become easier to spot in the sky. You may start to see it before sunset. As the days go by, instead of seeing it for only an hour or so, you will see it for 3 or 4 hours.

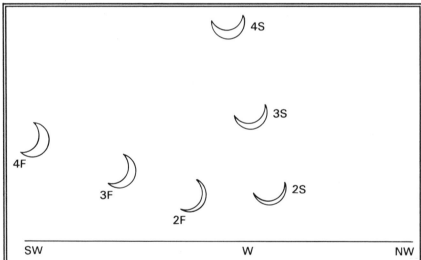

The Young Crescent Moon Climbs Into the Western Evening Sky

The young crescent moon appears in quite different locations in the sky depending on the season of the year. From the latitudes of southern Canada and northern United States, the Moon climbs a steep path from night to night *in the springtime* and a very gradual path *in the fall*. The moon's approximate locations above the western horizon about an hour after sunset are shown for 2-, 3-, and 4-day-old Moons in early spring (2S, 3S and 4S) and in early fall (2F, 3F, and 4F). Note that as the moon climbs in the sky, its crescent is becoming larger or "waxing". During winter and summer, the crescent moon climbs along a pathway that is between those shown for spring and fall.

On about the date of First Quarter, the moon will be about 1/4 of the distance around the sky (as measured from the sun) in its orbit around the earth. Half of the moon's disk now appears lighted — the half that is westward or to our right as we look at the sky. At sunset the moon will now appear up in the sky in the South (since the moon rose at about mid-day). You can expect that the moon will set at about midnight.

Between the Time of First Quarter and Full Moon

During the week from First Quarter until Full Moon you will see the lighted part of the moon growing and becoming much brighter. Now it is called a "gibbous moon" or a "waxing gibbous moon". Gibbous is the term used when the lighted part of the moon is more than half the disk. It is now much easier to see in the daytime. At sunset a bright moon is seen first in the southern sky. Later as the week goes by, it is seen in the southeastern sky, and then in the eastern sky just before the time of Full Moon. As this week goes by, expect to see the moon setting later and later, between midnight and the time of sunrise. In other words, it will set just a short while after midnight on the first day or two after First Quarter, and almost at the time of sunrise on the day or two before Full Moon.

On the day of Full Moon, expect the great round moon at its very brightest to rise approximately in the east at about the time of sunset. It will be in the sky all night, and highest at about midnight, and it will set in the west at about the time of sunrise.

Between the Time of Full Moon and Last Quarter

During the week between the times of Full Moon and Last Quarter, the lighted part of the moon gets smaller. It is now called a "waning moon" - meaning one that is growing smaller. It is called a "gibbous moon" at this time also, but it looks different from a "waxing gibbous moon". Now the "bright side" of the moon is on the left as we see it, or to the East, if we refer to the directions in the sky. Putting the two ideas together, we call it a "waning gibbous moon". As the week goes by, the moon interferes less with our observing if we want to observe faint objects in the evening or early night, since the moon rises later and later every night. On the first night or two after Full Moon, it will usually rise within an hour or two after the time of sunset, and it will be highest in the sky an hour or two after midnight, and set in the west an hour or two after sunrise.

The Beginner's Observing Guide

As the week goes by, the moon rises later and later until near the time of Last Quarter, when it rises at about midnight. During this week also, you should expect to see the moon in the daytime before noon in the southwestern or western sky.

On the day of Last Quarter, you can expect that the moon will rise at about midnight or a little after, will be highest in the sky at about the time of sunrise or a little after, and will set at about noon. Be sure to look for the moon in the southwestern or western sky a couple of hours before noon. It may be a challenge sometimes, but you may also be able to see it easily at other times.

Between the Time of Last Quarter and New Moon

During the period of time between Last Quarter and New Moon, the moon is waning fast; it is becoming a small crescent again.

It does not interfere with the observing plans of most observers because it is not seen in the evening sky at all and is seen only after midnight, or in the "wee hours" of the morning, or in the early dawn when it sometimes presents a very beautiful sight.

In the first few days after Last Quarter the moon rises in the east within a few hours after midnight and is highest in the sky a few hours after sunrise and sets in the early afternoon. As the week goes by, the moon continues to rise later and later. Two or three days before New Moon, the moon rises just a couple of hours before sunrise. Within the last few days before New Moon, it is a crescent that is growing smaller and smaller in the eastern part of the sky and it disappears from view when the sun rises. (The "brighter part" of the moon appears so small that the moon's overall brightness is much less than it was a week or so earlier.) Now the "horns of the crescent" are pointing upward away from the sun or to the south or southwest — toward the observer's right. In the last two or three day before New Moon, the moon's crescent is so small that many people will not see it at all. Even experienced observers may see it only for a short time, unless they are using binoculars to spot it and follow it as it moves up in the sky before the sun rises. On the last day before New Moon, when it appears very close to the sun, probably no one will see it rise just a short while before the sun.

Of course, on the day of New Moon, we do not observe the moon at all, except on the rare occasions when we see a solar eclipse. Now that the moon is back to New Moon, we are ready to begin the lunar cycle all over again.

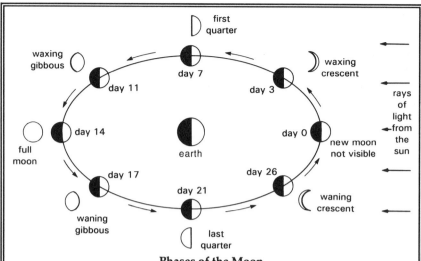

Phases of the Moon

This diagram shows the Moon at eight points in its orbit around the Earth, as viewed from a point high above the orbit. Imagine yourself an observer on Earth at the centre of the diagram and looking toward the moon at intervals of a few days. The outer figures show the appearances of the phases of the moon as viewed by an observer on Earth, at the corresponding times during the lunar month. Note that at New Moon the lighted side of the moon is not seen from earth. At the times of First and Last Quarter (Day 7 and Day 21), only half of the lighted half of the moon is seen. At the time of Full Moon (Day 14), all of the moon's lighted half is seen. The time between phases is approximate; the exact time from one New Moon until the next is slightly more than 29 1/2 days.

Dates of Moon Phases in 1994

The above guidelines for observing the moon are for any year. To help you apply these guidelines *during 1994*, here is a list of the dates when New Moon, First Quarter, Full Moon, and Last Quarter occur:

NEW MOON	FIRST QUARTER	FULL MOON	LAST QUARTER
			Jan. 4
Jan. 11	Jan. 19	Jan. 27	Feb. 3
Feb. 10	Feb. 18	Feb. 26	Mar. 4
Mar. 12	Mar. 19	Mar. 27	Apr. 3
Apr. 11	Apr. 18	Apr. 25	May 3
May 10	May 17	May 25	June 2
June 9	June 16	June 23	July 1
July 8	July 15	July 22	July 30
Aug. 7	Aug. 14	Aug. 21	Aug. 29
Sept. 5	Sept. 12	Sept. 19	Sept. 27
Oct. 5	Oct. 12	Oct. 19	Oct. 26
Nov. 3	Nov. 10	Nov. 18	Nov. 25
Dec. 2	Dec. 10	Dec. 18	Dec. 25

Dates of New Moon and Full Moon in 1995

To help apply the above guidelines, here are the dates of New Moon and Full Moon in 1995. Many ordinary calendars give the dates of First Quarter and Last Quarter. You may fill them in on this chart, if you wish.

NEW MOON	FULL MOON
Jan. 1	Jan. 16
Jan. 30	Feb. 15
Mar. 1	Mar. 17
Mar. 31	Apr. 15
Apr. 29	May 14
May 29	June 13
June 28	July 12
July 27	Aug. 10
Aug. 26	Sept. 9
Sept. 24	Oct. 8
Oct. 24	Nov. 7
Nov. 22	Dec. 7
Dec. 22	

Dates of New Moon and Full Moon in 1996

These are the dates of New Moon and Full Moon in 1996. Add the dates of First Quarter and Last Quarter, if you wish.

NEW MOON	FULL MOON
	Jan. 5
Jan. 20	Feb. 4
Feb. 18	Mar. 5
Mar. 19	Apr. 4
Apr. 17	May 3
May 17	June 1
June 16	July 1
July 15	July 30
Aug. 14	Aug. 28
Sept. 12	Sept. 27
Oct. 12	Oct. 26
Nov. 11	Nov. 25
Dec. 10	Dec. 24

Guide to the Map of the Moon

To assist in your observations of the moon, especially if you are using binoculars or a small telescope, the accompanying map is provided. With it are listed some of the many named features on the moon. They include craters, mountains, and maria. Craters are roughly circular features, many of which have been made by the impact of meteors and asteroids striking the surface of the moon over many millions of years. The maria (a Latin word meaning "seas") are not seas or oceans at all, because there is no water on the moon, but they are the large dark areas probably formed by the flow of lava billions of years ago.

The numbers before the names of the features indicate their position by number on the map of the moon. No 0's are used in the numbers to avoid confusion with the round craters marked on the map. The numbers after the features refer approximately to *the number of days after the new moon* when that feature is best seen in binoculars or a small telescope. Most observers prefer to observe craters and mountains when they are near the terminator (the line dividing the dark side from the light side). At the time of First Quarter, as seen from the earth, this line is nearly straight and is seen running from the moon's north pole to its south pole.

For several reasons, these numbers are only approximate. They are given in the form "7-8" meaning that you should try to find this feature *about 7 or 8 days after the date of New Moon*", which is approximately when the terminator or "sunrise line" will be crossing that feature.

For some features, two sets of numbers are given. This means that there are two times when this feature may be seen near the terminator. For example, after the crater Hercules, are the numbers "3-4" and "15-17". This means that this crater is near the terminator or "sunrise line" about 3 or 4 days after New Moon, and it is near the "sunset terminator" about 15 to 17 days after New Moon or several days after Full Moon. You will soon notice that, if you wish, you may study many features between the time of New Moon and Full Moon when the "sunrise terminator" is crossing them *or* later in the moon's month when the "sunset terminator" is crossing the same place. Of course, if you study the features later in the moon's month, you will have to observe later in the night when the waning moon is in the sky.

Features Marked on this Map of the Moon

Craters

21 Albategnius (7-8)

22 Alphonsus (8-9)

23 Arago (5-6)

24 Archimedes (8-9)

25 Aristarchus (11-12)

26 Aristillus (7-8)

27 Aristoteles (5-6)

28 Arzachel (8-9)

29 Atlas (15-16)

31 Autolychus (7-8)

32 Bessel (6-7)

33 Bullialdus (9-10)

34 Cassini (7-8)

35 Catharina (5-6)

36 Clavius (9-10)

37 Cleomedes (15-16)

38 Cook (15-16)

39 Copernicus (8-9)

41 Cyrillus (5-6)

42 Delambre (5-6)

43 Endymion (3-4 & 15-17)

44 Eratosthenes (8-9)

45 Eudoxus (5-6)

46 Fracastorius (4-5)

47 Furnerius (15-17)

48 Gassendi (11-12)

49 Grimaldi (13-14)

51 Halley (7-8)

52 Hercules (3-4 & 15-17)

53 Herschel (8-9)

54 Hevelius (13-14)

55 Hipparchus (7-8)

56 Julius Caesar (5-6)

57 Kepler (11-12)

58 Langrenus (15-16)

59 Lansburg (9-10)

61 Longomontanus (9-10)

62 Macrobius (3-4)

63 Maginus (8-9)

64 Manillius (6-7)

65 Maskelyne (4-5)

66 Maurolycus (6-7)

67 Mersenius (11-12)

68 Newcomb (3-4)

69 Petavius (15-16)

71 Piccolomini (4-5)

72 Plato (8-9)

73 Plinius (5-6)

74 Posidonius (4-5)

75 Ptolemaeus (8-9)

76 Reinhold (9-10)

77 Ross (5-6)

78 Schickard (11-12)

79 Schiller (11-12)

81 Snellius (15-16)

82 Stevinus (15-16)

83 Taruntius (3-4)

84 Theophilus (5-6)

85 Timocharus (8-9)

86 Tycho (8-9)

87 Wilhelm (9-10)

Mountains

A Alpine Valley (7-8)

B Alps Mts. (7-8)

E Altai Mts. (5-6)

F Apennine Mts. (7-8)

G Carpathian Mts. (10-11)

H Caucasus Mts. (6-7)

K Haemus Mts. (5-6)

M Jura Mts. (10-11)

N Pyrenees Mts. (4-5)

R Rheita Valley (15-17)

S Riphaeus Mts. (9-10)

V Speitzbergen (8-9)

W Straight Range (9-10)

X Straight Wall (8-9)

Y Taurus Mts. (3-4 & 16-18)

Z Teneriffe Mts. (8-9)

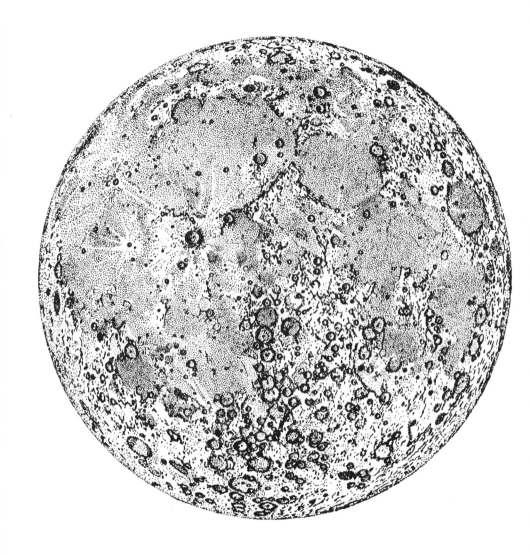

Moon as Seen from Earth

The Beginner's Observing Guide

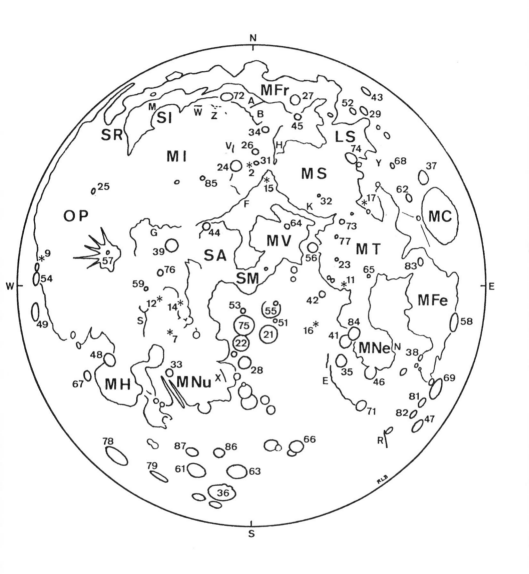

The Moon   See List of Named Features

"N" and "S" Indicate Approximate
Position of North and South Poles

Maria

LS	Lacus Somniorum (Lake of Dreams) (3-4 & 15-17)
MC	Mare Crisium (Sea of Crises) (3-4 & 15-17)
MFe	Mare Fecunditatis (Sea of Fertility) (3-4 & 15-17)
MFr	Mare Frigoris (Sea of Cold) (7-8)
MH	Mare Humorum (Sea of Moisture) (11-12)
MI	Mare Imbrium (Sea of Rains) (8-9)
MNe	Mare Nectaris (Sea of Nectar) (4-5)
NNu	Mare Nubium (Sea of Clouds) (8-9)
MS	Mare Serenitatis (Sea of Serenity) (4-5 & 16-18)
MT	Mare Tranquillitatis (Sea of Tranquility) (4-5 & 16-18)
MV	Mare Vaporum (Sea of Vapors) (7-8)
OP	Oceanus Procellarum (Ocean of Storms) (10-12)
SA	Sinus Aestuum (Seething Bay) (8-9)
SI	Sinus Iridum (Bay of Rainbows) (9-10)
SM	Sinus Medii (Central Bay) (8-9)
SR	Sinus Roris (Bay of Dew) (13-14)

Sites Associated with Various Lunar Missions

2	Luna 2, First to reach the Moon (Sept. 1959) (in MI)
7	Ranger 7, First close pictures (July, 1964) (between MNu and OP)
9	Luna 9, First soft landing (Feb. 1966) (in OP)
11	Apollo 11, First men on Moon (July 1969) (in MT)
12	Apollo 12, (Nov. 1969) (between MNu and OP)
14	Apollo 14, (Feb. 1971) (between MNu and OP)
15	Apollo 15, (July 1971) (near Apennine Mts.)
16	Apollo 16, (Apr. 1972) (near Crater Halley)
17	Apollo 17, (Dec. 1972) (between MS and MT)

Chapter 12

Observing the Planets in 1994, 1995, and 1996

Some of the easiest objects in the sky to observe are the members of our own Solar System. The Solar System is made up of the Sun at the centre, the nine major planets (counting Earth) and their moons or satellites, thousands of minor planets, or asteroids, and comets, and a great quantity of tiny dust particles.

Of the nine planets, five (not counting Earth) can be easily observed with the unaided eye because they are very bright objects. Two others are bright enough to be seen with binoculars. Only one planet, far-away Pluto, is too faint to be seen in binoculars and can be seen only with a large telescope.

Venus is immediately recognized because it is brilliantly white and much brighter than any star in the sky.

Jupiter, too, is whitish and brighter than any star, even Sirius.

Mars is usually an orangish-brown colour and can be about as bright as Sirius when it is near the earth, but at other times, it can be much less brilliant, even fading to about the same brightness as Dubhe, the star at the end of the cup in the Big Dipper.

Saturn is often seen as slightly yellowish in colour and varying from about the brightness of Rigel, the brightest star in Orion, when it is most brilliant, to the brightness of Spica, the brightest star in Virgo.

Mercury sometimes appears with the brightness of the stars of the Big Dipper, and sometimes it is even brighter than Sirius, the brightest star of all, but usually its great brilliance is not noticed because it appears in the twilight where its dazzling brightness cannot be appreciated.

The planets are different from the stars and other objects in the night sky. Because they travel around the sun, we cannot mark them on an ordinary star map and say that they will be seen in a certain place at a certain time of year. We need to describe their positions in a different way because their motion around the sun means that they will be in a different place from year to year, and from month to month.

The following information is about where and when the planets may be seen from 1994 through 1996. It begins with the planets that are closer to the Sun than Earth is, that is, Mercury and Venus. Then it gives information about the planets that are further away from the Sun than Earth is, that is,

Mars, Jupiter, and Saturn. Finally, information is given, in a general way, about where Uranus and Neptune are, but you will need binoculars and an additional star map to locate these two planets.

Mercury in 1994

Mercury may be seen low *in the western sky after sunset* for the following periods of time in 1994:

(a) during late January and early February,
(b) during May and early June,
(c) in late August, throughout September, and in early October,
(d) in late December.

Of these four periods of time the best for observers in North America is the second one. The *best* time of all in 1994 to see Mercury after sunset is *during the month of May.*

Mercury may also be seen low *in the eastern sky before sunrise* for the following periods of time in 1994:

(a) in the month of March, except for the first few days, and early April,
(b) during mid-July,
(c) during mid-November.

Of these three periods of time the best is the last one. The *best* time of all in 1994 to see Mercury before sunrise is during *mid-November.*

Mercury in 1995

Mercury may be seen low *in the western sky after sunset* for the following periods of time in 1995:

(a) during early January,
(b) in late April and throughout most of the month of May,
(c) during the last half of August and most of September,
(d) in late December.

Of these four periods of time the best is the second one. The *best* time of all in 1995 to see Mercury after sunset is *in late April and early May.*

Mercury may also be seen low *in the eastern sky before sunrise* for the following periods of time in 1995:

(a) in late February and during most of March,
(b) in late June and early July,
(c) from mid-October until early November.

Of these three periods of time the best is the last one. The *best* time of all in 1995 to see Mercury before sunrise is during *late October.*

Mercury in 1996

Mercury may be seen low *in the western sky after sunset* for the following periods of time in 1996:

(a) during the first week of January,
(b) from the second week of April until the end of April,
(c) during the last half of August and first week of September,
(d) during the last two weeks of December.

Of these four periods of time the best is the second one. The *best* time of all in 1996 to see Mercury after sunset is *in late April.*

Mercury may also be seen low *in the eastern sky before sunrise* for the following periods of time in 1996:

(a) in the last half of February and during the first week of March,
(b) during the first three weeks of June,
(c) during the first week of October.

Of these three periods of time the best is the last one, that is, in the early mornings of *the first few days of October.*

Venus in 1994

During January, February, and March, Venus slowly climbs into the western evening sky after sunset. Its brilliant light dominates the western sky after sunset during the entire spring and summer months. Finally by late October it disappears from the western evening sky.

By mid-November it may again be seen very low in the eastern sky a short while before sunrise. By December it is a bright and prominent object in the eastern sky for over an hour before the sun rises.

Venus in 1995

Venus is a very bright and prominent object in the morning sky before sunrise from January until July, 1995. In early July it is very low in the eastern morning sky and is not easily seen. Venus is not seen during August.

In September it emerges again in the western sky after sunset. It becomes more noticeable and brilliant in the western evening sky during October, November, and December.

Venus in 1996

Venus is a very brilliant and prominent object in the evening sky after sunset from the beginning of January 1996 until early June. It is at its greatest height above the western horizon at sunset in March and April, when it is half-way between the horizon and the zenith. In April and May it is bright enough to be seen at the time of sunset if conditions are good, and some people should be able to see it before sunset if they look in the right place. In mid-June Venus becomes difficult to see because it is in approximately the same direction as the sun. By the last week of June it is easy to spot this very bright object low in the eastern morning sky before sunrise. From early July until the end of the year, Venus is found in the eastern morning sky. It moves higher and higher and rises noticeably earlier each morning from mid-July until early September when it is half-way between the horizon and the zenith at sunrise. It is very brilliant during July, August, and September, and continues almost as bright for the remainder of the year.

Mars in 1994

Mars is not seen during January and February in 1994 because it is almost in the same direction as the sun. For the remainder of the year it can be seen only in the morning sky. During March it may be seen in the constellation Aquarius low in the eastern sky before sunrise. During April, May, and June it moves through the constellation Pisces which is also seen in the east in the early morning sky. During July and August, Mars may be seen moving through the constellation Taurus which rises after midnight and is in the sky until dawn. Observers should try to notice it during these two months as it moves past the Pleiades and north of the bright star Aldebaran. During September and October it moves through the constellations Gemini and Cancer, and may be seen in the early morning sky before sunrise. Try to watch it move past the bright stars Castor and Pollux. In November and December it moves through the constellation Leo and past the bright star Regulus. It may be seen in the late night sky in the east since it rises before midnight.

Mars in 1995

The first part of 1995 is an excellent time to observe Mars since it is favourably placed in the evening sky. During the first six months of the year, Mars is found in the constellation Leo, except for the period of time in February and March when it moves through the stars of Cancer and then back to Leo. During May, it is easy to observe moving past Regulus, the brightest star in Leo. In July and August as it appears to move eastward from the constellation Leo into Virgo, it is low in the west and southwestern sky in the evening. In September and October as it moves into the constellation Libra, it is low in the southwest after sunset and becomes more difficult to observe. During November and December it is too close to the direction of the Sun to be easily visible.

Mars in 1996

During the first five months of 1996 Mars is too close to the direction of the sun to be easily visible. In mid-June early morning observers may be able to spot the red planet among the stars of the constellation Taurus low in the eastern sky at the beginning of morning twilight. Throughout the remainder of the year, Mars is found in the eastern sky rising from one to two hours before the sun and visible in several constellations until morning twilight causes it to disappear. Observers should look for it in the following constellations: Taurus in June and July, Gemini in August and early September, Cancer in late September and early October, Leo from late October until mid-December, and Virgo in late December.

Observers should note Mars near the Pleiades in mid-June and near Regulus, the brigtest star in the constellation Leo, in early November.

Jupiter in 1994

During the first six months of 1994, Jupiter is found just west of the two brightest stars of the constellations Libra. Its brightness makes it easy to locate in this part of the sky which does not have any extremely bright stars. It is about half way between the bright stars Spica in Virgo and Antares in Scorpius. During January and February it rises in the east after midnight. From March until June it is easily found in the southern sky during the evening and early night hours. In July, August, and September it is low in the southwest after evening twilight. During October and early November, it will not be easily seen because of being in the same general direction as the Sun. In December it is visible low in the eastern sky before sunrise and it appears east of the main stars of Libra and moving slowly toward the stars of Scorpius.

Jupiter in 1995

During most of 1995, Jupiter is found in the constellation Scorpius — generally in the northern part of that constellation between its brightest stars and those of the constellation Ophiuchus. Keen observers should try to note its eastward motion among those stars during the months January to April and then its westward motion (sometimes called "retrograde motion") from May until August. During January and February it is seen low in the southeastern sky before sunrise. In the spring months it is seen rising in the southeast after midnight. In June, July, and August it is up in the southern sky at sunset and it sets in the southwest later in the night. During September and October it is very low in the southwest at the end of evening twilight. In November and December it is difficult to observe Jupiter because of its being in the same general direction as the Sun.

Jupiter in 1996

During 1996, Jupiter is found in the constellation Sagittarius — in the northern part of that constellation above the large configuration of stars called "the teapot". Observers should try to note its eastward motion in relation to nearby stars when obseving it before the month of May and then its westward motion (sometimes called "retrograde motion") when observing it from June until early September. Eastward motion may then be detected from October until December. During January and February it may be seen very low in the southeastern sky for a short while before sunrise. In the spring months it is seen rising in the southeast after midnight. In June, July, and August it is up in the southeastern sky at sunset and it sets in the southwest later in the night. During September, October and November, it is low in the southwestern sky at the end of evening twilight and sets shortly after. In December Jupiter is not seen because of being in the same general direction as the Sun.

Saturn in 1994

Saturn is found among the stars of the constellation Aquarius during all of 1994. In January it is seen low in the southwest after sunset. It is not seen in February, but becomes visible in the eastern morning sky before sunrise in March. Spring and summer are the best times to observe this planet, particularly July, August, and September when the constellation Aquarius is seen in the sky all night. In October, November, and December, it is in the southwestern sky after sunset and sets in the west several hours later.

Saturn in 1995

Saturn is found in the constellations Aquarius and Pisces in 1995. During the course of the year it moves slowly eastward from the bright stars in the northern part of Aquarius to the faint stars that form the circular outline (called "the Circlet") of one of the fish of Pisces. This circular outline is seen just below the Great Square of Pegasus. In January the planet can be seen low in the southwestern sky after sunset. It is not seen in February. By late March it is visible in the eastern morning sky before sunrise. During April,

May and June, it rises earlier each night: before 2:00 a.m. by mid-May and at midnight by mid-June. It is very easy to observe Saturn during July and August when it rises during evening twilight and can be seen in the sky during the entire night. In October, November, and December it is visible in the evening sky and sets later in the night.

Saturn in 1996

Saturn is found in the constellation Pisces in 1996. During the course of the year it moves slowly eastward from the bright stars in the northern part of Aquarius to the faint stars that form the circular outline (called "the Circlet") of one of the fish of Pisces. This circular outline is seen just below the Great Square of Pegasus. In January and February, the planet can be seen low in the southwestern sky after sunset. It cannot be seen in March and early April because of being in the same general direction as the Sun. In late April it is visible in the eastern morning sky before sunrise. During May it rises in the east about two hours before the Sun and by mid-June it rises about midnight. In July and August it can be seen in the sky during the entire night. In September, October, and November, it is visible in the evening sky and sets later during the night. During December it is in the southern sky at sunset and sets about midnight.

Uranus and Neptune in 1994, 1995, and 1996

Uranus and Neptune are generally considered too faint to be seen with the unaided eye, although a few people claim to have seen Uranus without optical aid. Both planets may be seen in binoculars, though they usually look just like stars. A telescope of moderate size shows them to be small disks, rather than just tiny dots. In 1994 and 1995, both Uranus and Neptune may be found among the stars of the eastern part of constellation Sagittarius, about half-way between the "teapot" configuration of stars and the stars of the constellation Capricornus. In 1996 Uranus is further eastward in the sky among the stars of the constellation Capricornus — below the two stars at the tip of the "western horn" of Capricornus (as shown on Maps 4 and 5). In 1996, Neptune is still in the constellation Sagittarius — about two-thirds of the way between the "teapot" configuration and the stars of Capricornus. These parts of the sky are best seen in the late evening during the summer months. For those who wish to search for Uranus and Neptune with binoculars or a small telescope, a map showing their exact location may be found in the *Observer's Handbook*, another publication of The Royal Astronomical Society of Canada.

Pluto in 1994, 1995, and 1996

Pluto is far too faint to be seen with the naked eye or with a pair of binoculars. Even in the largest and best telescopes in the world it appears as only a tiny dot of light. It is difficult to distinguish it from the millions of faint stars that also appear as dots of light, unless a person observes it with a large telescope for several nights in a row and notices that one of the tiny dots has moved. Then the person knows which one is Pluto. During 1994, 1995, and 1996, astronomers who have learned the exact position of Pluto and want to find it in their telescopes will be looking toward an area in the sky between the bright stars of the constellations Libra and Ophiuchus. (This area is best seen on Maps 3 and 4.) The months of April, May, and June are the best for observing this part of the sky. Maps showing the precise location of Pluto among the stars are published in astronomy magazines and in the *Observer's Handbook* of The Royal Astronomical Society of Canada.

Chapter 13

Observing Eclipses in 1994, 1995, and 1996

During some years, Canadians are lucky and have a chance to observe an eclipse right from their backyard. During other years there are no eclipses that are visible from this part of the world. Sometimes, however, there are parts of eclipses that are visible from parts of the country and they can easily be seen if the weather is good. In these cases, your luck depends completely on where you live and the type of weather you have.

Observers are encouraged to note carefully the dates of eclipses *and* mark them on a calendar so that they do not miss them.

The major eclipses visible from Earth are called *Solar Eclipses* and *Lunar Eclipses*.

A *Solar Eclipse* occurs at least twice during a calendar year and at the time of a New Moon. It happens because the Moon passes between the Sun and the Earth and hides at least part of the Sun from our view. Some solar eclipses are seen by no one or only a few people because they are visible only from certain remote places on Earth.

There are several kinds of Solar Eclipses. (i) The best known are Total Eclipses, in which the sun is totally hidden by the Moon as seen from certain places on Earth. The last Total Solar Eclipse visible from Canada occurred in 1979. (ii) Partial Solar Eclipses are ones in which the view of the sun is partly hidden for some locations on Earth. (iii) There are also Annular Eclipses, occurring when the Moon is a little farther from the earth than usual so that it appears a little smaller than usual; in this case, during an eclipse, the Moon cannot completely cover the sun. When this kind of eclipse happens, a "ring of the Sun" can be seen around the Moon, when viewed from some locations on earth.

A *Lunar Eclipse* may occur only at the time of a Full Moon, and it happens when the Moon partly enters or passes through the shadow of the Earth. Lunar Eclipses are usually easy to see if the Moon is visible in the sky, but they cannot be seen during daylight hours, because the Full Moon is not in the sky during the daytime. Such eclipses would be visible from other locations on Earth.

The main types of Lunar Eclipses are (i) Total Lunar Eclipses, in which the Moon completely enters the shadow, or umbra, of the Earth and the whole disk of the Moon becomes dark, (ii) Partial Lunar Eclipses, in which the Moon partly enters the earth's shadow or umbra and only part of the Moon's disk appears dark, and (iii) Penumbral Lunar Eclipses in which the Moon enters the faint "outer shadow" or "partial shadow" that surrrounds the umbra.

The Eclipses of 1994

In 1994 there will be two Solar Eclipses and two Lunar Eclipses.

The *two Solar Eclipses* are:

(1) an *Annular Solar Eclipse on May 10.*

This eclipse will be visible throughout Canada and the United States as a partial eclipse with part of the sun's surface covered by the moon, and in a pathway running from the southwestern United States to Nova Scotia, there will be an annular eclipse which means that for a few minutes the sun will look like an "annulus" or ring, because all of the sun's disk except a thin outer ring will be covered by the moon's disk. In Ontario, the path along which the annular eclipse will be visible will be along the extreme southern border of the province, crossing parts of Lake Erie and Lake Ontario.

Remember to *use extreme caution when trying to observe the sun.* Observing the sun *even during the annular phase* is just as dangerous as observing the Sun when there is no eclipse occurring. Refer to the chapter on observing the Sun to learn how to observe it safely.

(2) a *Total Solar Eclipse on November 3.*

This eclipse will be visible in the central part of South America and over parts of the South Atlantic Ocean. It will *not* be visible from North America.

The two Lunar Eclipses are:

(1) a *Partial Lunar Eclipse* on the night of *May 24-25.*

This eclipse will be visible throughout most of North America. Part of the Moon's disk will be inside the Earth's shadow for 1 hour and 44 minutes. Observers should try to note the Earth's shadow gradually crossing the craters on the southern part of the Moon. The moon will start to enter the Earth's shadow at 10:38 p.m. Eastern Daylight Time, and will leave the Earth's shadow at 12:22 a.m. Eastern Daylight Time. (Observers in other time zones should make the necessary adjustments according to the time zone in which they live.)

(2) a *Penumbral Lunar Eclipse* on the night of *November 17-18.*

Observers in almost all of North America may be able to see this very faint kind of lunar eclipse, if they observe the Moon very carefully. The northern part of the Moon's disk will be passing through the Earth's penumbra, which is the outer "partial shadow". Maximum eclipse, or the time when the Moon's disk is most in the "partial shadow", is at 1:45 a.m. Eastern Standard Time. Some observers may detect a very slight darkening of the northern part of the Moon about a half-hour or more before maximun eclipse and may continue to notice the darkening up to a half-hour or more after maximum eclipse.

For North American eclipse observers, 1994 is an unusually interesting year. The most important eclipse events are: (1) the Annular Solar Eclipse of May 10 which will be seen as a partial eclipse over the entire continent, and (2) the Partial Lunar Eclipse on the night of May 24-25.

The Eclipses of 1995

In 1995 there will be two Solar Eclipses and two Lunar Eclipses.

The *two Solar Eclipses* are:

(1) an *Annular Solar Eclipse on April 29.*

This eclipse will be visible in parts of South America. It will *not* be visible from Canada or the United States.

(2) a *Total Solar Eclipse on October 24.*

This eclipse will be visible in parts of Asia, from Iran through India to Vietnam. It will *not* be visible from North America.

The two Lunar Eclipses are:

(1) a *Partial Lunar Eclipse* on the night of *April 14-15.*

This eclipse will be visible over the Pacific Ocean and in Australia and the countries of the Far East. Only those Canadians living in the western part of the country will see any of the eclipse before the Moon sets, and they will see only the beginning. In the United States also, only those in the western part of the country will see it. The Moon's disk enters the Earth's umbra or shadow at 5:19 a.m. Pacific Daylight Time on the morning of April 15.

(2) a *Penumbral Lunar Eclipse* on *October 8.*

Observers in Asia and Australia may have a chance to see this very faint kind of lunar eclipse. It will *not* be visible from North America, since it will occur at about mid-day in the Western Hemisphere.

1995 is not a good year for North American eclipse observers, unless they are willing to travel great distances. Only those observers on the west coast will have a chance to catch a short glimpse of the Partial Lunar Eclipse on the morning of April 15.

The Eclipses of 1996

In 1996 there will be two Solar Eclipses and two Lunar Eclipses.

The *two Solar Eclipses* are:

(1) a *Partial Solar Eclipse on April 17.*

This partial eclipse of the Sun will be visible from New Zealand and from some islands in the South Pacific Ocean. It will *not* be visible from any parts of North America.

(2) a *Partial Solar Eclipse on October 12*.

This partial eclipse of the Sun will be visible in northeastern North America and in parts of Europe and North Africa. Weather permitting, the partial eclipse will be visible north of a line from central Nova Scotia to northern Lake Winnipeg in Manitoba, including parts of northern Ontario, northern Quebec, northern New Brunswick, Prince Edward Island, Newfoundland, Baffin Island and other islands of the Eastern Arctic. No eclipse will be visible from western Canada, nor from southern Ontario. The only part of the United States to see any of the eclipse will be the extreme northern tip of Maine.

The two Lunar Eclipses are:

(1) a *Total Lunar Eclipse* on the night of *April 3-4*.

This eclipse will be visible in the eastern parts of Canada and the United States. In many parts of Central and Western Canada and the United States, the Moon will rise while the eclipse is well in progress or near completion. Observers along the Atlantic Coast will be treated to a period of totality lasting about 85 minutes and beginning about 8:28 p.m. Atlantic Daylight Time. Weather permitting, it should be an interesting spectacle, and possibly a rather dark eclipse.

(2) a *Total Lunar Eclipse* on the night of *September 26-27*.

Observers in almost all of North and South America, weather permitting, will be able to see a long and interesting total eclipse of the Moon. Only those in the western parts of Canada and the United States will miss part of the beginning of the eclipse. Those in the eastern parts of North America will see the spectacle with the Moon well up in the sky. The following times for this event are given in Eastern Daylight Time. (Adjustments should be made by observers who live in all the other time zones.) The first contact of the Moon with the Earth's shadow is at 9:13 p.m.. Totality begins at 10:20 p.m.. Mid-eclipse is at 10:54 p.m.. Totality ends at 11:28 p.m.. Last contact of the moon with the earth's shadow is at 12:35 a.m. on September 27.

1996 is a good year for observing lunar eclipses with parts at least of two total eclipses visible from many regions of Canada and the United States.

Chapter 14

Observing Meteors and Meteor Showers

As our planet Earth travels around the Sun every year, it meets up with large amounts of dust, usually tiny particles that are no bigger than a grain of sand. These pieces of dust are called meteoroids. A strange event occurs when one of these particles and the earth's atmosphere encounter each other. The fast movement of the particle through the atmosphere causes the surrounding air to glow brightly. As astronomers say, the air surrounding the fast moving dust particle is being "ionized". When we look up at this event from below, we see a meteor flashing across the sky. Many people used to call them "shooting stars" or "falling stars". Actually, it is more correct to avoid these names and use the proper term — "meteors". Stars are extremely distant and very massive objects like our sun, usually many times more massive than our Earth. Meteors are glowing particles travelling through our Earth's atmosphere.

Observing meteors is easy and fun. It does not require binoculars, or a telescope, or any special equipment. However, you do concentrate on a certain area of the sky for up to an hour at a time, in order to get a good idea of the number of meteors flashing through the atmosphere. In this way meteor observing can be challenging. It will also help an observer to become more familiar with the sky and the constellations.

Meteors can appear on any night of the year, but, as we will see later, they are much more common at certain times of the year. They are more likely to be seen on nights when there is no Moon in the sky and when you are observing in a dark country location far away from the bright street lights of a city. Under such conditions, at times when there is no meteor shower at all, an observer can expect to see from 5 to 8 "sporadic" or stray meteors per hour. In fact, that number increases after midnight.

Sometimes we may see extremely bright meteors that are brilliant enough to cast a shadow on the ground. These are called fireballs or bolides, especially if they appear to break up into several pieces. Sometimes they even "explode" into a number of fragments. Occasionally, too, they appear to glow in different colours, such as green or red. Sometimes a trail, called a train, is left behind when the original flash from the meteor has disappeared. This train, which may appear slightly smokey, may last for five or ten seconds or even longer, if the meteor has been an extremely bright one. If we notice any of these events accompanying a meteor, we should carefully record it (or them), and we should note particularly the position in the sky and the time when the meteor was seen.

Meteors are most common on certain special "shower" nights during the year, when the earth encounters a stream of meteoroids or dust particles. We can tell when this is happening because, after observing for a while, we will see that most of these "shower" meteors appear to come from a single location in the sky. We say that they are "radiating" from that point in the sky, and that point is called the "radiant".

"Meteor showers" are usually named after the constellation in which the radiant is found. The constellation name has an "id"-ending. For example, the Leonids radiate from a spot in the constellation Leo. From the list below, it can be seen that two showers are called Aquarids. These are distinguished by naming the stars in Aquarius near which the radiants are found — delta and eta. The Quadrantids are named after a constellation that is no longer recognized; it was located near Bootes.

Here is a list of some of the main "meteor showers" during the year:

The Quadrantids

Early in January each year, the earth runs into a special stream of meteors, and if we are observing at exactly the right time, we may see up to 50 meteors per hour. However, such a large numbers is usually seen only for several hours on *January 3rd or 4th*. Unless the moon is out of the sky on that particular night and unless the maximum period occurs at night, instead of during daylight hours, this shower will be missed by most people. Another reason that many people miss this interesting shower is that the weather is often very cold in early January, and also there may be cloudy skies at that time of year.

An April Shower: The Lyrids

We have to wait almost four months for the next good meteor shower to occur — the Lyrids. This shower offers us about 15 meteors per hour when they are observed under good conditions on the night of their maximum, about *April 22* each year.

A May Flower: The Eta Aquarids

This is one of the two annual showers that are believed to originate from dust particles in the path of the famous Halley's Comet. They may sometimes be seen from April 21 to May 25, with the maximum around *May 3 to 5*. These meteors appear as very fast streaks and the brightest of them sometimes leave long-lasting trains (faintly glowing trails that linger in the sky).

The Delta Aquarids

A delight to observe, this shower reaches its maximum about mid-summer (*July 29*) meaning that it is ideal to observe on summer vacation. These meteors are relatively slow and offer an hourly rate of up to 20 under good viewing conditions.

A Midsummer Night's Dream: The Perseids

This shower can be a magnificent spectacle. You may see Perseids coming in rapid succession, followed by slack periods with little activity. You may also see "firework" Perseids, when two or more meteors appear almost simultaneously and fly off in different directions. Fireballs, bright enough even to cast a shadow, are seen from time to time. They may be seen over a period of many nights but the maximum occurs about *August 12*.

The Orionids of Fall

Like the Eta Aquarids, these meteors come from the stream of dust particles associated with the path of Halley's Comet. Often as many as 25 meteors per hour are seen. They are easily identified, not only from their radiant near Orion, but also from their rapid speed. Maximum activity occurs about *October 22*.

The Taurids

This shower's maximum rate is 15 per hour, *between November 1 and 3*. These are the slowest meteors of all the major showers. Fireballs reported in the months of October, November and December might belong to this stream.

The Leonids

This moderately active shower has a normal maximum rate of 15 per hour for a person who is observing alone about *November 18* each year. However, every 33 years the earth crosses the densest concentration of meteors and a real "meteor storm" often occurs, during which the number of meteors is measured, not in meteors per hour, but in meteors per second. In 1966, some observers in some places estimated the number they were seeing to be over 40 per second!

Winter's Graceful Geminids

This is now the major shower of the year. The Geminids offer a maximum of as many as 75 per hour, and they stretch out for two and a half days on either side of the maximum, *December 14*. The night before and the night of maximum are often the best nights of the year for high totals. Their relatively slow speeds add to the fun of watching this magnificent shower.

Whether you are observing a specific meteor shower, or just spending part of a night watching for any meteors that might happen to appear, you would be wise to follow a few suggestions in order to make your experience as profitable as possible:

1. *Plan* your observing session as you would other observing sessions, knowing when the moon will rise or otherwise possibly interfere with your plans. Moonlight greatly lowers the number of meteors you may see in a given period of time.

2. Rather than standing, use a *reclining lawn chair*. Adjust the back of the chair so that you are facing an area of the sky that is 45 to 55 degrees above the horizon.

3. *Dress warmly* so that you will be comfortable while observing. Have an extra sweater or jacket available since the temperature may drop considerably during the night. Observing from a reclining position may mean that you will feel the cold sooner than if you were standing.

4. Do not try to observe the entire sky. If you are observing at a time other than at one of the major meteor showers, choose the darkest area of the sky, that is, the area with the least light pollution. Face in that direction so that you can comfortably see about *a quarter of the sky*, and record the number of meteors that appear in that area over a one-hour or two-hour period. If you are observing at the time of one of the major showers, face, not exactly in the direction of the constellation from which the meteors are radiating, but about 50 to 60 degrees away from that constellation, and if possible, toward the darkest part of the sky.

5. Try to develop *a system of recording* the meteors seen. Some beginning observers merely count the number of meteors seen in a one-hour period. This is the minimum that you should try to do. Other more advanced observers use a tape recorder to record the number of meteors, the brightness or magnitude of each one, and any special features observed, such as "unusually fast" or "with a train that lasted for five seconds". Some observers use a star map to record the meteors by drawing the path of each one. During meteor showers they soon notice that almost all the meteors can be traced back to the "radiant". The problem with drawing while observing is that, unless the path is marked quickly, the observer may miss other meteors. One reason for observing in groups is that one person can act as a recorder while the others continually watch the sky.

6. *Take a break* after the end of each hour's observing. Move around in order to keep warm. A person's concentration drops if he or she tries to observe for a very long period of time. Note carefully the times when

you were observing, so that the numbers of meteors seen can be recorded in one-hour time periods.

It is very easy to enjoy meteor watching. With no special equipment required, no one should miss the chance to observe a meteor shower.

Chapter 15

Observing the Aurora

People who have never seen a beautiful aurora have missed one of the fabulous spectacles of nature. The dancing, shimmering rays and curtains of the aurora borealis are a thrilling sight to see in the northern sky. Without warning, the sky can suddenly come alive with a flood of red, green, purple, and yellow patterns that are fascinating to watch whether it is for an hour or a whole night.

One of the things that makes the aurora so fascinating is the fact that it is often quite unpredictable. Sometimes when we think a fabulous light show will last all night, it may last for only a few minutes or a half hour. At another time when we think it is a weak show and will soon die away, it bursts into action and lasts for hours, or even the whole night, or longer. During April 1981, there was a huge outburst of auroral activity which lasted for more than a week. Of course, it was not actually seen during daylight hours because of the brightness of the sun, but night after night, as soon as the sky was dark, the aurora continued.

What is the aurora? The word aurora is the Latin word for "dawn" or the "glow of daylight". Aurora borealis ("northern dawn") or the northern lights are words that are used to describe the glow or the brightness that often appears in the northern part of the sky over the northern latitudes of the Earth. This brightness or glow is most often seen over Canada, Alaska, Greenland, and the Scandinavian countries. A similar event occurs over the very southern latitudes of the globe where the sky brightness is called the aurora australis ("southern dawn") or the southern lights.

For hundreds of years people have asked what is the cause of these strange, weird, and wonderful lights that frequently filled the northern sky and sometimes covered almost the whole sky. We are still asking the same question, because even yet we do not *completely* understand the operation of the aurora. We do know that the light of the aurora is caused when energy is released as the upper part of the earth's atmosphere (100 kilometres or more above the earth) is bombarded by extremely tiny particles in the solar wind. These very minute particles are electrons and protons — much smaller than atoms. It is activity on the sun that causes the solar wind. An outburst of particles from the sun, known as a solar flare, and sometimes associated with a large sunspot or group of sunspots, can cause huge numbers (billions upon billions) of these tiny particles to flood out into space. When this "flood of particles from the Sun" reaches the Earth, there will be increased activity as they interact with the particles in the Earth's magnetosphere. The magnetosphere is a magnetic field that surrounds the Earth. There is always some interaction between the solar wind and the Earth's magnetosphere. This constant interaction causes an auroral ring above the northern part of the earth and centred over the Arctic islands of northern Canada, but most people in North America have never seen this glow. Observers in southern Canada and northern United States can expect to see the aurora only at times of increased solar activity, such as at those times when a solar flare occurs. At those times, the bright glow of the aurora extends further south. Sometimes after a very large burst of solar activity, the aurora can be seen as far south as Mexico, Cuba, Central America, and the Caribbean, but such events happen only rarely.

What produces the varying colours of the aurora? Scientists who have studied the aurora for many years are able to associate certain colours with the kinds of atoms that have caused the glow in the upper atmosphere. They have learned that red and green colours are produced by atoms of oxygen that have become luminous like the gas in a fluorescent light fixture. Blue is produced by nitrogen molecules.

Even though *we cannot predict exactly when there will be an aurora visible at a certain location*, there are a few facts that will help us to understand when we *might expect to see one*. We know that there is the greatest chance of seeing an aurora at the times *when the sun is very active*. As a result of observing the sun and studying it over the last two hundred years, astronomers now know that the sun's activity varies on about an 11-year cycle with the number of sunspots very low at the beginning and end of the cycle and the sunspot numbers very high near the middle of the cycle. During the years 1985 and 1986 the numbers of sunspots and the amount of solar activity was generally low. It was the beginning of an 11-year cycle. During 1989, 1990, and 1991 there were large numbers of sunspots. It was near the middle of the cycle, and the sun was very active. There were numerous displays of the aurora. *During 1994 to 1996* we can expect that the amount of activity on the sun will decrease greatly from what it was in 1990 and 1991. We can therefore, *expect to see the aurora borealis on only a few occasions* from the latitudes of southern Canada and northern United States.

In auroral displays many different auroral patterns are possible. The most common pattern in mid-northern latitudes is a steady white *glow* in the north. Sometimes over the course of a night, the glow increases in size and brightness, and spreads out from the north until it reaches from east to west and up as high as the North Star, or even the zenith, and it may become so bright that it is difficult to see many of the stars in the northern half of the sky. Another common pattern of aurora is called the *arc*. It may look like a slightly flattened arch in the northern sky; sometimes there may be two or three of them, one above the other, and they may be combined with a glow underneath. A third pattern is seen when auroral activity is strong. "*Rays*" or "*spikes*" may shoot up into the sky. They are most commonly seen in the north, from northwest to northeast, but may sometimes be found in other parts of the sky. They sometimes may "shoot up" to the zenith. A fourth pattern, seen at times of increased auroral activity, is the "*band of flame*"; it looks like the flames of a large fire shooting up into the sky. It may appear as a pulsation that spreads quickly upward over a large area of the sky with repeated flaming pulsations following at intervals of a second or less. Another pattern, much less common in southern Canada than northern Canada, is what looks like a great *curtain* or drapery hanging in the sky. Varieties and combinations of these and other patterns can be seen on any one night.

When should a person look for the aurora? The best advice for those who want to see this spectacle is just to *check* the sky, particularly the northern sky, *every clear night*. The next best piece of advice is to join an astronomy club where you can keep in contact with members who are interested in observing and monitoring the activity of the sun. These people will know when the number of sunspots is great, and perhaps when solar flares occur. If they know *when a solar flare has occurred*, they may agree to inform you and other members; you then ought to *check the sky* for an aurora *over the next few nights*, because there will be an increased possibility that you will see one then.

Enjoy the aurora whenever you see it. It is one of nature's most beautiful spectacles.

Chapter 16

Observing Comets

Comets are visitors from the outer reaches of our solar system. They are large "dirty snowballs" made of frozen gases and dust, and they are often several kilometres in diameter. The frozen materials are water ice, ammonia, methane, and other compounds. Most comets spend their lives at great distances from the sun, far too distant to be seen from the earth. Occasionally, a comet never before seen by humans is deflected toward the sun and begins its long journey on a great looping orbit around the sun. Only when it is relatively near the sun is it discovered by a keen-eyed observer and then seen by hundreds or thousands of other amateur astronomers and other interested observers as well.

Some comets are surprise visitors, totally unexpected. Others are familiar visitors that human beings have seen many times before; perhaps their first visit to the inner part of the solar system was thousands of years ago. By now their orbits are well known and predictable, and we can know precisely when their next appearance will be . Depending on the size of the orbit, it may take from a few years to millions of years for a comet to complete a single journey around the sun. Those that take less than 200 years are called periodic or short-period comets; others are called long-period comets.

As comets approach the sun, a change takes place. Their solid icy surfaces are heated and turned to gas. Around the solid inner core which is known as the *nucleus*, the gas, along with dust rising from the icy surface, forms a cloud. It is only the fuzzy cloud of gas and dust, called the *coma*, not the nucleus, which is seen when we oberve a comet sweeping across the sky. In some cases, enough gas and dust is produced to form a noticeable *tail* which can stretch out into space for millions of kilometres. The tail consists of two parts — the *gas tail* and the *dust tail.* The gas tail, often appearing bluish in photographs, points almost directly away from the sun. The dust tail, appearing whitish or yellowish because we see sunlight reflected from the dust particles, presents a slightly curved appearance because it lags behind the rest of the comet in its orbit.

There are several hundred known comets that have been discovered over the centuries of recorded history. Most are named after their discoverer. One exception to this rule is Comet Halley, perhaps the most famous comet of all, one that makes its appearance every 76 years. It is named after Edmond Halley, the first person to predict its reappearance, which he did in the eighteenth century. It was last visible in 1985, 1986, and 1987 when it was close enough to the earth to be seen in binoculars and telescopes; it was also seen with the naked eye for a much shorter period of time. In about the year 2060 and 2061, amateur astronomers will again be excitedly viewing its return to the region of the inner solar system.

Previously unknown comets can appear at any time and from any direction in the sky. In fact, in the last few years there have been many more new comet discoveries than would have been predicted from the number of discoveries in previous years. Many of these comets have remained close enough to the sun and earth to be seen by observers for several months; in a few cases they could be seen for almost a year. Most comet discoveries are made by amateur astronomers because professionals do not have the time to spend to long hours patiently searching the sky. A few of the comets discovered in recent years, though originally seen in fairly large telescopes, became bright enough within several months to be easily seen in binoculars. One or two of them could be seen with the naked eye. The best recent example was Comet Levy (also called 1990c). It was a beautiful naked-eye sight during August 1990 when it was in the constellations Delphinus and Aquarius. As the letter "c" in its name indicates, it was the third comet discovered in 1990; it was discovered by a Canadian, David Levy, who has now discovered a total of 18 comets. His many long hours spent searching the sky have been duly rewarded.

What comets can we expect to observe during the years 1994 through 1996? There are several comets that are predicted to be in the region of the sun and earth that are also predicted to be bright enough to be seen in telescopes owned by amateur astronomers. Information about them can be found in *The Observer's Handbook* and in astronomy magazines. There is, of course, also the possibility that one or several "new" comets will be discovered, which will become bright enough to be seen in binoculars or with the unaided eye — as happened in 1990 with Comet Levy. News of such events are known by members of most astronomy clubs soon after such discoveries are announced.

Chapter 17

Observing the Zodiacal Light

On the clear moonless nights in late winter and early spring there is a strange light that can be seen in the western sky about an hour and a half after sunset. It is much larger and sometimes much brighter than most people realize; yet few people have seen this strange large light. Many people also do not know that it is really very easy to see, if they are away from city light pollution and have a good view of the western horizon.

What is this strange light that makes its appearance on clear spring nights in the western sky? It is a phenomenon known as the *zodiacal light*, and it actually appears, not just in the western sky after twilight in the springtime, but also before dawn in the morning sky during the late summer and autumn. This very large area of sky brightness is caused by tiny dust particles orbiting the Sun. Our solar system has not just planets and comets and asteroids, but also a great ring of dust in the region of the inner planets. When sunlight strikes these trillions of tiny dust particles, it is reflected from them just as it is when it strikes the Moon or the planets. And just as the sunlight striking the Moon (three or four days after New Moon allows us to see it as a crescent) in the western sky, so also the sunlight striking the ring of dust allows us to see it.

Exactly when and where should I look for the zodiacal light? The answer is you should look for the evening zodiacal light *in the western sky from 1 1/2 to 2 1/2 hours after sunset* during the months of February and March at times when there is not a bright Moon in the sky. The morning zodiacal light may be seen *from 2 1/2 to 1 1/2 hours before sunrise in the eastern sky* during the months of September and October at times when the sky is clear and moonless. The reason you do not observe it within 1 1/2 hours of sunset or sunrise is that a glow seen at that time above the horizon is indistinguishable from the glow of twilight. A bright Moon in the sky also prevents us from seeing the Zodiacal Light, just as it hinders a good view of the Milky Way.

What should we expect to see? If the sky is clear, you can expect to see a large triangle or pyramid of light whose base is about 60 degrees wide along the western horizon (if it is the evening zodiacal light) and whose upper point is about 60 degrees above the western horizon. In other words, during February, it extends upward about as high as the Pleiades 1 1/2 hours after sunset. The upper point is not exactly above the centre of the base of the triangle, but somewhat to the left, so that the triangle seems to be slightly tilted to the south. The triangle of light observed as the morning zodiacal light is similarly tilted to the right or to the south. Within this large area you will see a glow or brightness that may occasionally be as bright as the Milky Way, depending on the observing conditions, though usually it is not that bright. However, under some superb viewing conditions, I have actually seen it considerably brighter than the Milky Way. This glow or brightness may last for a couple of hours, depending on the observing conditions, but usually after an hour or so it becomes more difficult to see.

After you have learned to recognize the zodiacal light at the appropriate time of year, you will wonder why you did not notice this strange, fascinating glow in the sky long before you did.

Chapter 18

Observing the Sun Safely

Many people think that astronomers study only the stars, planets, and other objects in the night sky. In fact, many observers regularly study the sun during daylight hours.

The sun is our nearest star. It is the centre of the solar system to which our Earth belongs. It has produced the light and energy that have enabled life to emerge on Earth. It makes possible the production of our food and everything else that we see on Earth. Therefore, it is certainly reasonable to study the sun and learn as much as we can about it.

Before anything else, several warnings must be given about observing the sun.

1. NEVER look directly at the Sun with the unaided eye.

2. NEVER look at the Sun when using binoculars or a telescope, unless you are absolutely certain that you are using the correct kind of solar filter.

    The Sun must be treated with great respect. Even the briefest glimpse at the Sun, when using any kind of optical aid without the proper filter, can focus enough heat and light into the eye to cause permanent eye damage or permanent blindness. It is not just at times of a solar eclipse that viewing the Sun can be dangerous; such an idea is nonsense.

Looking at the sun, without the protection of a proper filter, is ALWAYS DANGEROUS.

Safe viewing of the sun can be done in a limited number of ways:

1. For direct viewing of the sun, you may use an arc welder's glass #14. This very dark glass may be purchased at welding supply outlets. Welder's glass with numbers other than 14 is not suitable. When using it, be sure that it is properly in place over your eyes before looking in the direction of the Sun.

2. You may construct a simple pin-hole camera, to project an image of the sun.

    Constructing a pin-hole camera is quite simple. Obtain a shoe box or one of similar size. Using a pencil, punch a small hole in the middle of one end of the box. Put a piece of white paper on the inside of the opposite end of the box. Turn the box upside down, and hold the box up so that the end with the pinhole is pointing toward the Sun. DO NOT LOOK THROUGH THE PINHOLE. Let the sunlight enter the box through the pinhole, and let the image fall on the white paper on the opposite end of the box. With your back to the Sun, you can now observe the image of the sun. You may possibly notice that the image shows one or several sunspots, if there are large ones on the Sun at the time of your observation.

3. You may use a mirror to project an image of the sun.

    Obtain a small mirror and a piece of cardboard the same size as the mirror. Make a hole 3 to 5 mm in diameter in the centre of the cardboard, and tape the cardboard over the mirror. Put the mirror in sunlight so that the light is reflected from the mirror onto a wall or flat surface. You will see an image of the sun. DO NOT LOOK INTO THE PATH OF SUNLIGHT REFLECTED FROM THE MIRROR. The quality of the image will be better if you project it onto a white wall or screen and if the surrounding area is dark. This method works well if the mirror is located in a window and the image of the sun is projected onto a white screen in a darkened room. The image may not be sharp, but it may be good enough to allow you to see sunspots if there are large ones on the Sun at the time.

4. When using a telescope, one kind of solar viewing which is safe is through a commercially produced solar filter designed to fit over the front end of the telescope. These very reflective metallic-coated glass filters reflect almost all of the sun's light back into space, and allow only a very tiny amount to enter the telescope. Such filters may be expensive, but the assurance of safety is worth the cost. If you use a

The Beginner's Observing Guide

filter of this kind, you should check it frequently to be sure that very tiny pin-holes do not appear in the metallic coating.

Solar filters which are designed to be used at the eyepiece end of the telescope *must not* be used. They are very unsafe because heating could cause them to crack or shatter, and instant and permanent eye damage could result. A few years ago this type of filter was sold with some telescopes. Anyone who owns such a filter should destroy it, and not use the telescope for solar viewing, unless a proper kind of filter can be obtained.

What can one see when observing the Sun? There are a number of things that you will notice:

1. The image of the Sun appears perfectly round. You will notice that this is true even if the hole in the pin-hole camera or in the cardboard over the mirror is not perfectly round. The Sun is actually a giant sphere which is much closer to being a perfect sphere than the earth is; the Earth, in fact, is larger around its equator than around the poles.

2. The image of the Sun appears slightly darker near the edge of the disk than at the centre. This is called "limb-darkening". There is a reason for this. When we look at the centre of the disk, we are looking more directly into various layers of the very hot gases in the outer parts of the sun, but when we look at the edge of the disk, we are looking across only the outermost layers which are not as hot and bright as the layers of gases further inside

3. There may be a small dark spot or spots visible on the disk of the Sun. Do not expect to see very many spots, certainly not as many as you may have seen on pictures of the Sun taken at large observatories, but you may see one or two, or even more depending on your method of observing. If you see any sunspots at all, you should repeat the observation the next day or on several following days, and record any changes you notice. Perhaps you will soon begin to learn something about the rotation period of the Sun and about the "life-cycle" of sunspots.

Many amateur astronomers observe the Sun every clear day and carefully record the number of sunspots and sunspot groups that they see. Over the years observers have noticed that there is an 11-year cycle, with few sunspots at the beginning and end of the cycle and large numbers near the middle of the cycle. Scientists have also learned that there is a relationship between solar activity and certain things that happen on Earth, such as the appearance of the aurora or northern lights. Observations of the Sun made by amateur astronomers with simple equipment have helped us to gain a better understanding of what is happening in the Sun. However, there is still a great deal to learn even about our nearest star.

Several excellent books are available to help you understand the activity of the Sun, the 11-year sunspot cycle, and other features that you may begin to observe on the Sun. Above all, exercise caution and follow the rules of safe observing when you study the Sun. In that way you can enjoy the experience.

Chapter 19

Where to Get More Information

This book is intended only as a very basic introduction to astronomy and the study of the night sky. As you become more familiar with the stars, planets, and other objects of interest, you will want to gain more knowledge about all of these things. Luckily there are many resources that you can turn to, in order to satisfy your curiosity.

(a) From Joining an Astronomy Club

There are many advantages to joining an astronomy club. You will meet people who will be able to assist you in finding the information you want. Most of the people you will meet have already been through the stages you are now going through, and they know how it feels to be unsure about where to get answers to certain questions.

In Canada, the largest organization of people who are interested in astronomy is The Royal Astronomical Society of Canada. This organization is over a hundred years old and it has over three thousand members. It has clubs called "Centres" in twenty-two cities all across Canada.

Here are some of the many advantages to joining the local club or Centre of The Royal Astronomical Society of Canada:

1. When you join you will receive two publications, each mailed to you six times a year. *The Journal of The Royal Astronomical Society of Canada* contains articles about astronomical discoveries, and about important people and events in the history of Canadian astronomy. "The

Bulletin" which is a national newsletter, reports recent happenings in the Centres across Canada and tells about events, such as summer "star parties", that are being planned for future months. It also contains short articles of current interest to observers across the country.

2. You will receive a copy of *The Observer's Handbook*. This is a very high-quality observing guide, loaded with many kinds of information, including star maps and many lists of interesting objects to observe. (Remember that the cost to non-members of this book alone is $16.00 per year, but you will have it included in your membership.)

3. You will receive your club or Centre's newsletter. It will tell you about the interesting things happening in your own area. The members of the club have a chance to write about what they have been observing lately. They may also write about what equipment they have bought or have built, and they may discuss whether they are satisfied with it.

4. By being a member of the R.A.S.C., you may receive discounts at certain retailers when you buy things that interest amateur astronomers. You will hear of items that are for sale much sooner than if you did not belong to a club. Several members of a club may wish to share in the purchase of a large or expensive item, and thus they may be able to save money. Some members have actually saved hundreds of dollars when they bought their equipment – because they belonged to a Centre.

5. You will have a chance to attend a regular organized program of free talks or lectures by both professional and amateur astronomers. Most of the Centres have at least one talk or lecture a month on some topic that interests the members. There are usually monthly meetings also, at which members discuss their recent and planned observations.

6. You will be able to share in the use of the Centre's telescope, or telescopes, or observatory, depending on the equipment owned by the Centre. Some of the Centres own beautiful observatories which the members have worked hard to build. They are happy to have interested beginners join in their observing programs.

7. You will have access to the R.A.S.C.'s library resources and the Centre's library. Many Centres have a very good libraries. Borrowing some of the books or other materials may save you from having to make costly purchases.

8. You will have access to the back-issues of the Centre's newsletters and to the newsletters from the other Centres across Canada. Many of these

other newsletters contain a great deal of important information. Most Centres receive the newsletters from the other twenty-one Centres across Canada.

9. You will be able to receive the advice of experienced amateur astronomers on observing, and astrophotography, and many other aspects of astronomy. Some members of the Centres are experts in certain areas because they have been interested in astronomy for many years. Their advice can be very helpful.

10. You will have the chance to attend and to vote at the R.A.S.C.'s annual General Assembly. This large three-day event is held in a different city across Canada every year. You will be able to hear talks and see projects and displays that have been prepared. The Society's annual awards are also presented. It is an opportunity to meet astronomers from all across the country, and to have some fun, too; there is even a humorous song contest.

11. There is the general opportunity for the exchange of ideas and friendship with many people who share an interest in astronomy. Within some Centres there are groups of members who are interested in observing certain kinds of objects, or in building telescopes, for example.

12. There is the chance for outings, field trips, and observing sessions with knowledgeable amateur astronomers. Many Centres have regular programs for observing at an observatory or "dark-sky" site away from the light pollution of a large city. These events include sessions for members, as well as sessions open to the public.

Certainly there are many benefits of joining the R.A.S.C. far beyond the small membership fee. Currently membership fees are less than $40 per year, and less than $25 for persons under 21 years (with proof of age required). Some of the Centres levy a small surcharge to cover the cost of maintaining their equipment.

The following is a list of the Centres of the R.A.S.C. and addresses:

Calgary Centre	c/o Calgary Centennial Planetarium, P.O. Box 2100, Calgary, AB T2P 2M5
Edmonton Centre	7112 – 137 Avenue, Edmonton, AB T5C 2L5
Halifax Centre	c/o N.S. Museum, 1747 Summer Street, Halifax, NS B3H 3A6
Hamilton Centre	P.O. Box 1223, Waterdown, ON L0R 2H0
Kingston Centre	P.O. Box 1793, Kingston, ON K7L 5J6
Kitchener-Waterloo Centre	c/o Mr. Jeff Brunton, 10 Dumfries Street, #7, Paris, ON N3L 2C6
London Centre	P.O. Box 842, Station B, London, ON N6A 4Z3
Société d'Astronomie de Montréal	C.P. 206, St. Michel, Montréal, PQ H2A 3L9
Montreal Centre	P.O. Box 1752, Station B, Montréal, PQ H3B 3L3
Niagara Centre	P.O. Box 241, Niagara Falls, ON L2E 6T3
Ottawa Centre	P.O. Box 6617, Station J, Ottawa, ON K2A 3Y7
Quebec Centre	C.P. 9396, Ste-Foy, PQ G1V 4B5
Regina Centre	P.O. Box 20014, Cornwall Centre, Regina, SK S4P 4J7
St. John's Centre	c/o Mr. Randy Dodge, 206 Frecker Drive, St. John's, NF A1E 5H9
Sarnia Centre	c/o Ms. Alice Lester, 1091 Emily Street, Mooretown, ON N0N 1M0
Saskatoon Centre	Sub P.O. No. 6, Box 317, Saskatoon, SK S7N 0W0
Toronto Centre	c/o McLaughlin Planetarium, 100 Queen's Park, Toronto, ON M5S 2C6
Thunder Bay Centre	Ms. Emilee Searles, 120 Riverview Drive, Thunder Bay, ON P7C 1R4
Vancouver Centre	c/o Gordon Southam Observatory, 1100 Chestnut Street, Vancouver, BC V6J 3J9
Victoria Centre	c/o Mr. Bill Almond, 354 Benhomer Drive, Victoria, BC V9C 2C6

| Windsor Centre | c/o Mr. C. Joady Ulrich, Secretary, 5450 Haig Ave., Windsor, ON N8T 1K9 |
| Winnipeg Centre | Room 110, St. Paul's College, 430 Dysart Road, Winnipeg, MB R3T 2M6 |

People who do not live near any of the above Centres, or who do not wish to attach themselves to one of the Centres, may join as "unattached" members of the R.A.S.C. by contacting the National Office of the Society at the following address:

> The Royal Astronomical Society of Canada,
> 136 Dupont Street,
> Toronto, ON M5R 1V2

In the province of Québec, in addition to the two Centres listed above, there is an organization, L'Association des Groupes d'Astronomes Amateurs (AGAA) which has clubs in many of the larger cities and towns. Its excellent monthly francophone publication is called "L'Astronomie Québec". More information about this organization may be obtained by writing to M. Jean-Marc Richard, 4545 Ave. Pierre-de-Coubertin, C.P. 1000, Succ. M, Montréal, P.Q. H1V 3R2.

(b) From Books

There are many books that can provide a more complete introduction to the night sky. This is a list of those that are especially recommended.

Bishop, Roy, ed. *The Observer's Handbook.* The Royal Astronomical Society of Canada, Toronto, Ont. This is one of the world's best annual guides to observing the night sky. It contains many lists of objects that can be used in observing projects, and a wealth of information about the night sky.

Dickinson, Terence. *Exploring The Night Sky: The Equinox Astronomy Guide For Beginners.* Camden House Publishing Ltd., Camden East, Ont. 1987. This short, well-illustrated guide to the sky is especially suitable for young people and beginners.

Dickinson, Terence. *Nightwatch: An Equinox Guide To Viewing The Universe.* Camden House Publishing Ltd., Camden East, Ont. 1983. This is a superb introduction to the art of observing the sky. The various chapters deal with many aspects of amateur astronomy. You will be proud to own this book.

Levy, David H. *Observing Variable Stars: A Guide For The Beginner.* Cambridge University Press, Cambridge. 1989. For those who are interested in the fascinating study of variable stars, there is no finer introduction available. This book shows the author's true love of the night sky and all its many objects, as well as his special fascination with variable stars.

Levy, David H. *The Joy Of Gazing.* The Royal Astronomical Society of Canada — Montreal Centre, Montreal. 1985. This small booklet provides very good suggestions for getting started in a regular program of observing the night sky.

Levy, David H. *The Universe For Children.* Everything In The Universe, Oakland, Ca. 1985. This book, though small, has many ideas about introducing children to the wonders of the heavens.

Levy, David H. and Edberg, Stephen J. *Observe Meteors.* Astronomical League, Washington, D.C. 1986. This booklet is filled with information about observing meteors and meteor showers.

Peltier, Leslie. *Leslie Peltier's Guide To The Stars.* Astromedia, Milwaukee, Wi. and Cambridge University Press, Cambridge. 1986. This is a very well-written book that can be helpful to those who explore the night sky with binoculars.

Peltier, Leslie. *Starlight Nights* Sky Publishing Corp. Cambridge, Mass. 1965. This is the autobiography of a man who truly loved the stars and joyfully observed the night sky for over sixty years.

Sherrod, P.C. *A Complete Manual Of Amateur Astronomy.* Prentice Hall, New Jersey, 1981. This is a very thorough guide to amateur astronomy. The chapter on solar observing can be particularly useful for those who choose to observe the sun.

Star Atlases

Every observer eventually wants to own a good star atlas. It provides the "roadmaps of the night sky". A good basic star atlas usually also provides lists of interesting objects to observe, as shown on each of its star maps. There are many star atlases available, some good and some not very good. The following is a list of four of the best available.

Bright Star Atlas 2000.0 by Wil Tirion. This inexpensive, excellent star atlas contains easy-to-read star charts and very useful lists of interesting objects accompanying each of the 10 star charts. These charts, covering the whole sky, show over 9000 stars and 600 deep-sky objects (star clusters, nebulae, and galaxies). This atlas is strongly recommended as a beginner's atlas.

The Edmund Scientific Mag Six Star Atlas by Terence Dickinson, Victor Costanzo, and Glenn F. Chaple. This very good sky atlas is spiral-bound and has 12 charts covering the whole sky, as well as 3 additional enlarged maps covering the Orion, Virgo, and Sagittarius areas of the sky. All the stars visible to the unaided eye under the best of conditions (magnitude 6.2) are shown, along with over 1000 objects of special interest (the brightest galaxies, nebulae, star clusters, and variable and double stars). There are also 34 pages of information that is very practical and useful for the observer whether observing with the unaided eye, binoculars, or a small telescope.

Norton's 2000.0 Star Atlas And Reference Handbook. ed. by Ian Ridpath. This is an updated version, the 18th edition, in fact, of a classic star atlas that has been a favorite for over 80 years. It is an ideal star atlas for a beginning observer and one that he or she can use for many years. The entire sky is shown on 8 charts. Over 8700 stars, to the faintest discernible with the unaided eye under the very best sky conditions (magnitude 6.5) are shown, as well as over 500 variable stars and over 800 deep-sky objects (star clusters, nebulae, and galaxies).

SkyAtlas 2000.0 by Wil Tirion. This is a more advanced star atlas, and is the kind that will be needed as you begin to observe fainter objects. There are 26 large-format charts that show the entire sky. This atlas is available in three versions. The Deluxe bound version has large folded charts that are colour-coded for different kinds of objects in the sky. The Desk Edition has unbound charts showing black stars on a white sky background. The Field Edition has white stars on a black sky background. All three editions show about 43,000 stars and 2,500 other deep-sky objects (star clusters, nebulae, and galaxies). The Field Edition is recommended for those who wish to take their star maps out to the observing site. The black sky background means that there will be less glare when you shine a flashlight on it. Some observers have found also that it is best to have the charts laminated, especially the ones that are frequently used. The laminated plastic coating prevents dew and frost from damaging the paper.

Books for the Binocular Observer

There are several good books that have been especially written for the person who observes the night sky with binoculars. Here are five of the best which are currently available. Owning at least one of them could be very helpful in planning binocular observing sessions. All can be ordered from Sky Publishing whose address is given in the next section.

Crossen, Craig and Tirion, Wil. *Binocular Astronomy*. Sky Publishing Corporation, Cambridge, MA. 224 pages. $24.95

Harrington, Philip S. *Touring The Universe Through Binoculars*. John Wiley And Sons, New York. 1990. 294 pages. $24.95

Kozak, John. *Deep-Sky Objects For Binoculars*. Sky Publishing Corporation, Cambridge, MA. 124 pages. $9.95

Moore, Patrick. *Exploring The Night Sky With Binoculars*. Cambridge University Press, Cambridge. 1986. 203 pages. $11.95

Muirden, James. *Astronomy With Binoculars*. 156 pages. $7.95

(c) From Magazines

One of the best ways to introduce yourself to the regular practice of observing the night sky, and certainly a great way to keep in touch with current developments in amateur astronomy, is to make use of the monthly magazines that are available. They may be found in local libraries, or bought at many newsstands, or ordered through subscription. In North America there are two major English-language magazines that are very popular among amateur astronomers. They are *Astronomy* and *Sky and Telescope*.

Astronomy is a non-technical, popular monthly magazine that is quite easily understood by the beginning observer. It has articles about the latest developments in astronomy and space exploration, and is filled with beautiful photographs. In the centre of each issue is a star map for the early-night sky of the current month and on it are marked the bright planets in their proper positions for the current month. Following the map are about ten or twelve pages explaining objects and events that may be observed with binoculars or telescope during the current month. These include planets, asteroids, meteor showers, and comets. There are usually articles about ways to improve your observing, and articles reviewing the latest equipment that astronomers may wish to buy. The annual subscription price is currently $24 in the United States and $33 in other countries. The address is Kalmbach Publishing Company, P.O. Box 1612, Waukesha, WI USA 53187-9950 (Telephone 800-446-5489)

Sky and Telescope is a more technical monthly magazine that is highly respected by many serious amateur astronomers. Each issue contains excellent articles about current happenings in astronomy and space science. It also has a map of the night sky for the current month and detailed information about the interesting objects to observe in the night sky. All of the information, whether book reviews, historical articles, or reports on the latest discoveries, are carefully and accurately written. The annual subscription price is currently $27 in the United States and $36.38 in Canada. The address is Sky Publishing Corporation, P.O. Box 9111, Belmont, MA. USA 2178-9111. (Telephone 617-864-7360)

(d) From Visiting an Observatory or Planetarium

(i) Observatories

Several astronomical observatories in Canada are open to the public at certain times. Some of these observatories receive visitors during the day at certain times of the year. For such occasions, guided tours may be available or may be arranged. *Some* observatories also are open to the public for a limited amount of nighttime viewing with a telescope. Such observing sessions may last for two or three hours, one night per week during the summer months. Always check with the individual observatory to find out if and when public observing times are scheduled.

The following is a list of some Canadian observatories (east to west across the country) with their addresses and phone numbers for obtaining information about tours, visits, and possible public observing sessions.

Burke-Gaffney Observatory, Saint Mary's University, Halifax, NS B3H 3C3
    Telephone (902) 420-5633

Observatoire Astronomique du Mont Mégantic, Notre Dame des Bois, PQ
    J0B 2E0 Telephone (514) 343-6718

National Museum of Science and Technology, 1867 St. Laurent Blvd,
    Ottawa, ON K1G 5A3 Telephone (613) 991-9219

David Dunlap Observatory, Box 360, Richmond Hill, ON L4C 4Y6
    Telephone (416) 884-2112

Hume Cronyn Observatory, University of Western Ontario, London, ON N6A 3K7 Telephone (519) 661-3183

Science North Solar Observatory, 100 Ramsey Lake Road, Sudbury, ON P3E 5S9 Telephone (705) 522-3701

Dominion Radio Astrophysical Observatory, Penticton, BC V2A 6K3 Telephone (604) 493-7505

Gordon MacMillan Southam Observatory, 1100 Chestnut Street, Vancouver, BC V6J 3J9 Telephone (604) 738-2855

University of British Columbia Observatory, 2219 Main Mall, Vancouver, BC V6T 1Z4 Telephone (604) 822-2802

Dominion Astrophysical Observatory, 5071 West Saanich Road, Victoria, BC V8X 4M6 Telephone (604) 363-0001

Well equipped amateur observatories are operated by many of the Centres of The Royal Astronomical Society of Canada. These observatories are generally open to the members of the individual Centre. (In some cases, a small annual fee, in addition to the membership fee, may be charged for the use of the equipment.) Belonging to an R.A.S.C. Centre and sharing in the use of the Centre's equipment is a great way to become acquainted with the fine equipment that the advanced amateur astronomers in some of the Centres are using. The best way to learn how to use such equipment properly is to share in an observing project when the equipment is being used by experienced amateur astronomers. Such people will probably have used the equipment many times to pursue their interest in the study of the heavens. Information about joining a Centre of the Royal Astronomical Society of Canada has already been given in a previous section of this chapter.

In most Centres new members may also make arrangements to see equipment that is privately owned and used by the more experienced members of the group, but such arrangements must be obtained on an individual basis, when a new member wishes to do this.

(ii) Planetaria
A visit to a planetarium can be an exciting educational adventure. Most planetaria (the proper plural of the word "planetarium") are able to use their special projectors to project a large map of the nighttime sky, with all of the visible stars and planets, on their dome-like ceilings. These large star maps projected on the huge domes give a very real picture of the nighttime sky. This method is much better than holding up a large instructional star

map, even a very large one. It is also much better than using an ordinary home or school projector to give a picture of stars and constellations. A planetarium's special projectors can show the whole visible sky as it appears at any time of the year and from any place on earth. These projectors are also used to present shows that demonstrate many things relating to the study of the stars, the planets, and space.

Here is a list of some of the planetaria in Canada (arranged from east to west across the country) along with their addresses and telephone numbers which may be used to obtain information about shows that are being presented.

The Halifax Planetarium, The Education Section of the Nova Scotia Museum, 1747 Summer Street, Halifax, NS B3H 3A6 Telephone (902) 424-7391

Dow Planetarium, 1000 St. Jacques Street W., Montreal, PQ H3C1G7 Telephone (514) 872-4530

McLaughlin Planetarium, 100 Queen's Park, Toronto, ON M5S 2C6 Telephone (416) 586-5736

Ontario Science Centre, 770 Don Mills Road, Don Mills, ON M3C 1T3 Telephone (416) 429-4100

W.J. McCallion Planetarium, Department of Physics and Astronomy, McMaster University, 1280 Main Street West, Hamilton, ON L8S 4M1 Telephone (461) 525-9140 Ext. 7777

Doran Planetarium, Laurentian University, Ramsey Lake Road, Sudbury, ON P3E 2C6 Telephone (705) 675-1151 Ext. 2222

Manitoba Planetarium, 190 Rupert Avenue, Winnipeg, MB R3B 0N2 Telephone (204) 943-3142

The Lockhart Planetarium, 394 University College, 500 Dysart Road, The University of Manitoba, Winnipeg, MB R3T 2M8 Telephone (204) 474-9785

Alberta Science Centre / Calgary Centennial Planetarium, 701 – 11 Street S.W., P.O. Box 2100, Stn. M, Calgary, AB T2P 2M5 Telephone (403) 221-3700

Edmonton Space And Sciences Centre, Coronation Park, 11211-142 Street, Edmonton, AB T5M 4A1 Telephone (403) 451-7722

H.R. MacMillan Planetarium, 1100 Chestnut Street, Vancouver, BC V6J 3J9 Telephone (604) 736-5656

The Beginner's Observing Guide

Most people enjoy a visit to an observatory or a planetarium. If there is one in your area of the country, plan to visit it soon. You will be glad that you did.

Chapter 20

Questions I Always Wanted to Ask About Astronomy

There are many questions that come to the minds of people when they begin to become interested in astronomy. Some of them are presented here along with suitable answers.

Q.: *Why does a Full Moon look so large when it is rising and much smaller when it is high in the sky?*

A.: This strange fact — that the moon looks very large when near the horizon — is called the "Moon illusion". The moon near the horizon is definitely not nearer to us than when it is high in the sky. In fact, our brain plays a trick on us. When we look toward the horizon we see trees and hills and houses and many objects spread over the landscape. Our mind must know that the moon is really the same size whether high overhead or near the horizon. Because of the objects on the landscape, there is a suggestion of great distance to the moon on the horizon. The mind then makes the moon on the horizon appear larger in order to be like the one it remembers seeing high in the sky. Yes, it is an illusion; the brain makes the moon look larger!

All extended objects look larger when near the horizon. Compare the appearance of the Big Dipper and Orion when near the horizon and when high in the sky. They too appear much larger when near the horizon. Try looking at the rising Full Moon through a long hollow tube; it will suddenly look smaller and just as it does when overhead, because with the tube you have cut off your view of objects on the landscape which cause the illusion.

Q.: *What is the Harvest Moon?*

A.: The Harvest Moon is the name given to the Full Moon nearest to the autumn equinox, which occurs about September 21 or 22. This Full Moon, then, is in either September or early October. For several nights after this Full Moon, the moon rises only 20 to 30 minutes later from night to night. (At most other times during the year the moon rises an average of 50 minutes later each day.) At this time of year, the path of the moon's orbit around the earth makes a different (smaller) angle with the line of the eastern horizon than at any other time in the year. This fact allows the moon, for several nights, to rise sooner than we would expect it. Long ago farmers said that these "quickly rising" moons in the early autumn gave them extra light when they needed it to finish harvesting their crops.

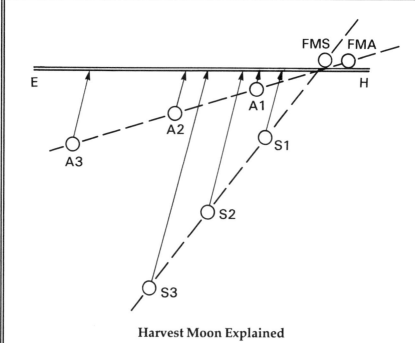

Harvest Moon Explained

The double line, EH, represents the Eastern Horizon, as viewed from southern Canada, at about the time of sunset. The dashed lines represent the moon's orbit in autumn and in spring. The circles, FMA, A1, A2, and A3, represent the rising Full Moon in autumn, and the Moon 1, 2, and 3 days later. The circles, FMS, S1, S2, and S3, represent the rising Full Moon in spring and the Moon 1, 2, and 3 days later. The autumn Moon rises more quickly from day to day because its path is closer to the horizon.

The Beginner's Observing Guide

Q.: *What is the Hunter's Moon?*

A.: The Hunter's Moon is the name given to the Full Moon which occurs one month after the Harvest Moon. For the same reason as mentioned on the previous page, the moon rises only 25 to 35 minutes later from night to night for several days after the date of this Full Moon. Hunters, as well as farmers, are thankful that these "quickly rising" moons in October or November give them some extra light after sunset.

Q.: *Why do stars twinkle?*

A.: Stars twinkle because the light we see coming from the stars travels through the atmosphere around the earth and there is turbulence in the Earth's atmosphere. Stars are enormously large compared to the Earth; many stars are much bigger even than our own sun. However, all stars are very, very far away from us. They are so far away that they appear as tiny dots or tiny points of light. As this light from the stars moves down through our Earth's atmosphere it meets turbulence that causes it to appear to "jiggle", just as light coming up through a rippling swimming pool on a hot day seems to jiggle. Some people have noticed that planets usually do not twinkle. The reason is that they are much nearer to us than any star. The planets, though they may seem to be just tiny dots to the unaided eye, are really little disks of light. Even though the little disk may jiggle because of turbulence, there is still one spot on the disk from which light is always coming.

Many people have said that it would be great to observe the sky from the Moon, which has no atmosphere. Then there would be no twinkling at all.

Q.: *What is a black hole?*

A.: Many astronomers believe that there are very dense objects in the universe, objects that are called black holes. An object is very dense if it is very massive or heavy for the volume of space that it occupies. (We would say that air is not very dense but marble and lead are dense.) Black holes may have been formed at the very early stages in the history of the universe, or when large stars go through a supernove explosion, or when an object like stars gathers into itself a great deal of mass from other stars. A black hole is so very massive that it has enormous gravity associated with it. (We know that the Earth, which is more massive than the Moon, has more gravity associated with it than the Moon does.) The gravity of a black hole is so great that *everything* in space around it is pulled into it, and is never seen again. In fact, the force of gravity is so great that even light itself cannot escape from the black hole. We can never "see" a black hole, as we can see a star like our Sun, if there is no light escaping from it. That is why it is "black", and why it is like a "hole in space". Astronomers must use other methods (other than direct optical viewing) to determine that a black hole exists; they must examine what is happening in the area around where it may exist. There is still a great deal to be learned about strange objects like black holes, and they will be discussed by astronomers for many years as we find out more and more about them.

Q.: *How far away is the nearest star? How long would it take to get there?*

A.: The nearest star to the Earth is our own Sun. Our Earth is part of the system of nine planets that travel around this great star. It takes light over 8 minutes to travel from the Sun to the Earth. The speed of light is 300,000 kilometres per second. The distance between the sun and the earth is about 149,600,000 kilometres. If we could travel in a space ship at a speed of 50,000 kilometres per hour, it would take us 125 days to reach the Sun.

Perhaps in your question you wanted to ask how far away was the nearest star beyond our Sun, and how long it would take to get there?

The star that is nearest to our Sun is the star that is called Proxima Centauri. It is 4.2 light-years away. That means that it takes light, travelling at 300,000 kilometres per second *over 4 years* to travel from that star to our earth. If we could travel in a space ship at a speed of 50,000 kilometres per hour, it would take us over 88,000 *years* to reach this star which is the *nearest* star of all to our sun.

Q.: *What are "deep sky objects"?*

A.: "Deep sky objects" is a term used by amateur astronomers to describe many kinds of objects that they observe in the night sky. The objects are all very far away and most of them are faint and challenging to see in binoculars or a telescope. The term includes star clusters, nebulae, and galaxies. Many of these objects are best seen with rather large telescopes which have greater light-gathering ability than smaller telescopes.

Q.: *What is the difference between a reflection nebula, an emission nebula, and a dark nebula?*

A.: Reflection nebulae are huge clouds of gas and dust that are located near stars. The gas and dust shine because they reflect the light from the nearby stars. An example is the nebulosity near the stars of the Pleiades; this can be seen in large binoculars or a wide-field telescopes used at low power.

Emission nebulae are clouds of gas and dust located near hot stars; the light from the stars energizes the gas and causes it to glow by fluorescence, as the gas in a fluorescent light glows. An example is the Orion Nebula; this can be seen with the unaided eye or in binoculars and is a very interesting object.

Dark nebulae are clouds of gas and dust which block the light coming to us from distant stars. The area of the sky looks dark only because we see stars from the surrounding area, but do not see the light from stars in the area of the gas and dust cloud. An example is the dark lane in the constellation Cygnus. Under good conditions it can be seen with the unaided eye.

Q.: *What is the meaning of the the terms "Right Ascension" and "Declination", which I often hear experienced amateur astronomers using?*

A.: These terms "right ascension" and "declination" are used when stating the position of an object in the sky. In Chapter Four we learned about a simple system of stating the location of an object in the sky; we used the horizon as a reference and gave the position of an object by saying it was in a certain direction as measured around the horizon (azimuth) and at a certain distance in degrees above the horizon (altitude). Another and more commonly used method of stating the location of an object in the sky is to use the equator as the reference. The equator of the sky, usually called the "celestial equator", is directly above the earth's equator, just as the celestial poles are above the Earth's poles. Declination is the distance, in degrees, of an object either north or south of the celestial equator. A declination of 45°N means that the object is 45° north of the celestial equator. When looking south in the winter sky we can visualize where the celestial equator is if we know that it runs approxiately through the belt of Orion. Right Ascension is the distance of an object, measured eastward along the equator, from the point called the Vernal Equinox, which is the apparent position of the sun on the celestial equator on March 21 each year. Rather than measuring in degrees, as rarely happens, Right Ascension is more commonly measured in hours and minutes, with 24 hours being the complete distance around the celestial equator. An object at 6 hours and 30 minutes would be 6 1/2 hours east of the Vernal Equinox, or a little over a quarter of the distance around the sky from the Vernal Equinox.

Q.: *How far can you see in a telescope?*

A.: This is a question that amateur astronomers are often asked. It is very difficult to answer precisely, and most amateurs prefer not to have to try to answer questions like this one. One way (and this is only *one* way) in which it could be answered would be to say that many amateur astronomers regularly observe galaxies, for example, which are extremely distant from our galaxy, the Milky Way. A few amateur astronomers also observe some of the quasars which are much more remote that most galaxies. As an example of the enormous distance of some galaxies, we may use the Virgo Cluster of Galaxies which are thought to be at least 40 million light-years away. An example of a quasar that can be seen in amateur telescopes is the one called 3C273 which is thought to be about 3 billion light years away, and it is probably one of the nearer quasars! Remember that a light year is the distance that light travels in one year, and that the speed of light is 300,000 kilometres per second. To express the distance to one of the Virgo galaxies in kilometres (which will make a ridiculously huge number — which astronomers try not to use), (1) you might find the number of seconds in a year (60 X 60 X 24 X 365), (2) multiply that number by 300 000 to obtain the speed of light in kilometres per year, and (3) multiply that number by 40 000 000 to obtain the approximate distance in kilometres to one of the galaxies that can be seen in Virgo. (The answer, a number with 21 digits, would be extremely cumbersome to use.) Perhaps we can now understand why astronomers use "light-years" rather than "kilometres" to describe the distances to galaxies.

Some astronomers would prefer to answer this question by saying that whether you can see a very distant object depends entirely on the brightness of the object. In some telescopes you may see a bright galaxy which is dozens of millions of light-years away, but a faint galaxy at only a fraction of that distance may not be detected at all.

Chapter 21

Suggestions for Brownies, Guides, Cubs, and Scouts

All members of the Scouting movement are encouraged to explore the wonders of nature. Recognizing and knowing something about the objects readily seen in the night sky means that the young person has taken a real interest in gaining a better understanding of the universe in which we live.

Brownies, Guides, Cubs, and Scouts have individual badge requirements for activities they undertake.

The following are the most recent requirements for astronomy-related badges for the individual groups. After each one of the requirements, some suggestions are offered to help the young person complete the required task.

For Brownies

1. *Have a session outdoors with an adult to look at the stars. Find the Big Dipper and the North Star.*

    For a good session at night under the stars you should contact a person who is very familiar with the sky — someone who knows the stars that can be seen at a particular time of year and the planets that are currently visible. Members of local astronomy clubs have people who are happy to share their interest and enjoyment of the night sky with young people.Contact the nearest Centre of The Royal Astronomical Society of Canada. All of the 22 Centres have members with considerable experience in showing the sky to beginners.

    Finding the Big Dipper and the North Star should be easy if you read and follow the instructions in Chapter Three of this book.

2. *Look at the stars through a telescope or field glasses, and, if possible, visit a planetarium or observatory.*

    Perhaps it is best to borrow a pair of field glasses or binoculars and look at what appears to be the brightest stars in the evening sky. Using a telescope is difficult for a beginner and should not be done except with the supervision of an experienced owner.

    If you have a chance to visit a planetarium or an observatory, do not miss it. You may be able to see a planetarium show that explains the stars and constellations that are currently visible in the evening sky. If there is a display gallery at the planetarium, take your time as you walk through it and read the information about the displays. You will learn a great deal. When planning to visit an observatory, try to arrange to do so at a time when there is a public viewing session or when a guided tour is being given. Check the appropriate section in this book for the list of planetaria and observatories in Canada. Check with the nearest Centre of The Royal Astronomical Society of Canada to see if that Centre has an observatory where a visit may be arranged.

3. *Explain why the Sun and stars appear to move across the sky.*

   To understand the rotation of the earth, read Chapter One of this book. Use a globe and turn it slowly. Imagine that a nearby house is the sun and that houses several kilometres away from you are other stars.

4. *Learn about the Milky Way, our solar system and the movement and phases of our Moon.*

   Build simple models of the Earth and Moon, and of the solar system. Start off by using a grapefruit as the Earth, an orange as the Moon, and a beach ball as the Sun. Find other objects to use as other planets.

   On a clear moonless night in the summer or winter, try to see the Milky Way, or have it pointed out to you by an experienced observer. Try to remember that the Milky Way is made up of billions of stars and our Sun is only one of them.

5. *What is a planet? What planet do we live on? Tell something special about three other planets.*

   You will be able to find many good books which give information about the planets. You may begin with Terence Dickinson's *Exploring The Night Sky.*

6. *Know why sailors in ancient times needed to know about the stars.*

   The stars provided the only "natural" way to find directions and navigate on the ocean. Even today, if modern technology fails, navigation by the stars can be used.

   Review Chapter Three to find the way to determine directions by the stars. You should know that for sailors in the southern hemisphere who cannot see the northern stars, there are other stars that can help them find their directions.

For Guides

1. *Tell what is meant by: Planets, Meteors, Stars, Comets, Meteorites, Milky Way.*

   There are many books which give information about these topics. Begin with a book like Terence Dickinson's *Exploring The Night Sky.*

2. *Draw a picture or make a model of our solar system. Show the different planets.*

   A model is better than a picture. You may begin by using a beach ball as the Sun. Use other smaller objects as the planets. Remember that Jupiter and Saturn are the largest planets. The object representing Earth must be much smaller than the ones used for these large planets.

3. *Tell how we can use the Sun and stars to tell directions.*

    Reread Chapter Three in this book.

    Remember that the Sun is like a star because it rises in the east and sets in the west, as the earth rotates.

4. *Explain the movement of the stars.*

    Reread Chapter One for an understanding of the daily movement of the stars, and Chapter Two for an understanding of the apparent movement of the stars as seen in the sky from season to season. Other books will give you information about the motion of stars, and about the movement of stars as our galaxy rotates. You should also know that the Milky Way Galaxy itself is moving and other galaxies are moving also.

5. *There are many ancient tales of how the constellations came to be. There are the stories of the Big Dipper and the Little Dipper, of Pegasus the flying horse, and many others. Learn one of these and tell it.*

    Modern astronomers do not need to know the ancient stories about the star patterns since they have nothing to do with the science of the stars. These stories were made up by people long ago who had very active imaginations and were able to imagine that they saw in the star patterns the shapes of the heroes and the gods they talked about in their mythology or religion.

    In this book, part of the story of the hero Perseus (from Greek mythology) is referred to in the section about the January-February Night Sky.

    The Big Dipper and Little Dipper are not constellations, but parts of the constellations called Ursa Major (the Big Bear) and Ursa Minor (the Little Bear). Most of the stories you will find in legends and myths refer to bears, not dippers. Pegasus, the flying horse, is associated with the story of Bellerophon, a proud hero of Greek mythology. This story can be found in most of the books on Greek mythology.

6. *Find these constellations: Cassiopeia, Ursa Major (which includes the Big Dipper).*

    These two constellations are found in the northern sky. Using the star maps in this book and the proper information for the time of year, you may be able to find these areas of the sky. If you live in a city, you will not be able to see all of the stars shown on the star maps because of the problem of light pollution.

7. *Also point out in season two of these constellations: Cygnus, Taurus, Leo, Orion, Pegasus, Gemini.*

Again, use this book to help you learn about when these constellations can be seen in the sky. Check with someone who knows the sky very well to be sure of identifying the proper area of the sky.
or
Find the stars of the Summer Triangle,
or
Find any two of the bright stars: Capella, Sirius, Arcturus, Antares, Aldebaran.
You may use the star maps and accompanying information in this book to find out when these stars can be seen in the night sky. Have your identification checked by someone who knows the sky very well.

8. *Find one planet in the night or morning sky.*

Complete this item by consulting Chapter 12 of this book. Remember that the brightest planets are Venus and Jupiter, but they are not always visible in the sky. Find out what area of the sky you should observe in order to see one of the planets at the present time.

For Cubs

According to *The Cub Book* published by the National Council of Scouts Canada, one of the nine possible activities, five of which the Cub must do to obtain an Observer Badge, is "recognize and point out four constellations."

Using the star maps in this book will help the leader and the young person to recognize many constellations during any time of year. Very distinctive constellations and star patterns should be used. Begin with the Big Dipper, but be sure to explain that it is not a constellation, but a large star pattern within the constellation Ursa Major, the Big Bear. The Little Dipper, also, is a star pattern within Ursa Minor, the Little Bear. Cepheus, the King, and Cassiopeia, the Queen, as well as Draco, the Dragon, are also constellations that are easily found in the northern part of the sky, and are visible throughout the year. Orion, the Hunter, is suggested as a winter constellation.

One of the possible requirements to earn the Green Star is the following: "Point out in the night sky six constellations or well known star figures, or make a map of the stars showing at least six constellations and the North Star."

Again, using the star maps in this book will help the leader and young person to recognize the constellations and star patterns. If the Cub member chooses to draw a star map, he should try to include constellations in the

The Beginner's Observing Guide

northern part of the sky in order to be able to include the North Star. He should begin by drawing a horizon line at the bottom of the page and marking the north point. Then he can mark the North Star, and then the bright stars of the constellations in that area of the sky.

For the Winter Cubbing Badge, one of the requirements is: "Point out the North Star and three winter constellations."

Using the star maps in this book, the leader and Cub member will see that in winter night sky the Big Dipper is standing up on its handle in the northeast, and the Pointer Stars direct you to the left to Polaris, the North Pole Star. Cassiopeia and Cepheus are easily found; they are westward from the Pole Star, as you see from Map 1 in this book.

For the Woodsman Badge, one of the requirements is: "Point out the North Star and three constellations."

Follow the same suggestions as given above but remember that, depending on the season and time of night, the northern constellations may not be in the same direction in the sky. Use the star maps in this book.

In the section, Know and Practise Your Wolf Cub Skills, one of the seventeen activities which Wolf Cubs are invited to learn is the following: Find directions from the stars.

You can find out how to find north and the other directions from the stars by reading and following Chapter Three in this book.

For Scouts

The badge requirements for Scouts are listed in the *Canadian Scout Handbook*, published by the National Council of the Boy Scouts of Canada. At the Gold Stage in the requirements for the Exploring Badge, Scouts are asked to "identify five stars or constellations."

Regardless of the time of year or the time of night, this book will help you to identify stars or constellations. Choose some of the brightest stars or most easily recognized constellations. Use the star maps in this book to verify your identification.

The *Fieldbook For Canadian Scouting*, published by the National Council of the Boy Scouts of Canada, has a section called "Heaven and Earth". The first edition, published in 1986, has diagrams showing the Big Dipper and some northern constellations, and also two small star maps showing some of the summer and winter constellations (pages 286 to 291). The two maps showing some of the stars of the summer sky should be used only in the early summer and at the times given. The winter star maps should also be used only in the early winter and at the times shown. These maps do not show most of the constellations in the eastern or western sky.

Scouts would be well advised to use, instead, the complete sky maps given in this book, not only because they show the complete sky but also because they can be used throughout all the seasons of the year. In the *Fieldbook*, some important constellations, such as Serpens, are not shown on the summer star map. On the winter star map in the *Fieldbook*, the constellations Triangulum, Eridanus and Monoceros are not shown.

Scouts would be well advised also to become much more familiar with the sky than the minimum requirements for their badge would suggest. If at all possible, they should use a book, such as this one, whenever they can, in order to acquaint themselves with the constellations and bright stars of the heavens.

Chapter 22

An Appendix of Useful Information

The Constellations

Constellations are areas or regions of the sky that have precisely defined boundaries. There are 88 constellations. As shown in Chapter 2, certain constellations can never be seen from mid-northern latitudes. These are in the areas of the sky above the region of the South Pole. Other constellations are in areas of the sky that never set. This chart names all of the constellations and gives information about finding them on the star maps.

Name	Where Found	Name	Where Found	Name	Where Found
Andromeda	1	Crux	S	Octans	S
Antlia	2	Cygnus	3	Ophiuchus	3
Apus	S	Delphinus	4	Orion	1
Aquarius	5	Dorado	S	Pavo	S
Aquila	4	Draco	C	Pegasus	4
Ara	S	Equuleus	4	Perseus	5
Aries	1	Eridanus	6	Phoenix	S
Auriga	1	Fornax	6	Pictor	S
Bootes	2	Gemini	1	Pisces	5
Caelum	1,S	Grus	5,S	Piscis Austrinus	5
Camelopardalis	1	Hercules	3	Puppis	1,S
Cancer	1	Horologium	S	Pyxis	2
Canis Major	1	Hydra	2	Reticulum	S
Canis Minor	1	Hydrus	S	Sagitta	4
Capricornus	4	Indus	S	Sagittarius	4
Carina	S	Lacerta	4	Scorpius	4
Cassiopeia	C	Leo	1	Serpens	3
Centaurus	3	Leo Minor	(1)	Sextans	2
Cepheus	C	Lepus	1	Taurus	6
Cetus	5	Libra	3	Triangulum	5
Chamaeleon	S	Lupus	3	Triangulum Australe	S
Circinus	S	Lynx	1	Tucana	S
Columba	1	Lyra	3	Ursa Major	C
Coma Berenices	2	Mensa	S	Ursa Minor	C
Corona Australis	4	Microscopium	S	Vela	2,S
Corona Borealis	2	Monoceros	1	Virgo	2
Corvus	2	Musca	S	Volans	S
Crater	2	Norma	S	Vulpecula	4

Notes:

— The number after the name of the constellation is the number of *one of the star maps* on which that constellation may be found. *Most* of the constellations may be found on *several* star maps. The number 1, for example, may mean that this constellation is found on star maps 1, 2, and 3.

— The letter *S* indicates that this is a constellation in the southern sky and is not well seen from the mid-northern latitudes.

— A number *and* the letter *S*, such as found after the constellations Puppis and Vela, indicates that *part* of the constellation is shown on one of the star maps, but that this southern constellation is *not completely* seen from mid-northern latitudes.

— The letter *C* after several of the constellations indicates that these are circumpolar constellations. When observed from mid-northern latitudes, they do not set. They will be found on *all six* star maps.

— The number (1) after Leo Minor indicates that this constellation is not marked on any of the star maps, but its area is shown on Map 1 and other star maps. It is located between Leo and Ursa Major, but it has no bright stars.

Basic Solar System Data

Object	Diameter (km)	Rotation Period (days)	Distance from Sun[2] (millions of km.)	AU[3]	Period of Revolution around Sun	Number of Satellites
Sun	1392000	25-35[1]				
Mercury	4878	58.60	57.9	0.39	87.97 days	0
Venus	12104	243.00	108.2	0.72	224.70 days	0
Earth	12756	1.00	149.6	1.00	365.26 days	1
Mars	6787	1.03	227.9	1.52	686.98 days	2
Jupiter	142800	0.41	778.4	5.20	11.86 years	16
Saturn	120000	0.44	1423.8	9.52	29.46 years	18
Uranus	51200	0.72	2868.7	19.18	84.01 years	15
Neptune	48680	0.67	4492.1	30.03	164.79 years	8
Pluto	2300	6.39	5926.5	39.62	247.69 years	1

Notes: 1. The rotation period of the sun varies with its latitude. The shortest rotation period occurs at the equator; the longest occurs at high latitudes. The rotation period of Jupiter, also, varies slightly depending on latitude.
2. The distances given are the mean (or "average") distances.
3. AU means Astronomical Unit(s). 1 Astronomical Unit is the mean (or "average") distance between Sun and Earth, 149.6 million kilometres.

List of the 30 Brightest Stars

This is the list of the 30 stars that have the greatest apparent brightness as seen from the earth. (Actually, the list includes 31 stars since it begins with our sun.) Many of these stars are marked on the star maps.

The number after each star is the apparent magnitude. The letter "*v*" indicates that the star varies in brightness. The letter "*S*" indicates that it is a star in the southern part of the sky and cannot be seen from the mid-northern latitudes.

Star	Apparent Mag.	
Sun	-26.70	
Sirius	-1.46	
Canopus	-0.72	(S)
α Centauri	-0.29	(S)
Arcturus	-0.06	
Vega	0.04	
Capella	0.08	
Rigel	0.14	
Procyon	0.37	
Achernar	0.48	(S)
β Centauri	0.60	(S)
Altair	0.76	
Betelgeuse	0.80	(v)
Aldebaran	0.85	
α Crucis	0.87	(S)
Spica	0.96	
Antares	1.00	(v)
Pollux	1.15	
Fomalhaut	1.16	
Deneb	1.25	
m Crucis	1.26	(S)
Regulus	1.35	
Adhara (ε CMa)	1.50	
Castor	1.58	
Shaula (λ Sco)	1.62	
Bellatrix (γ Ori)	1.63	
γ Crucis	1.64	(S)
El Nath (β Tau)	1.65	
Miaplacidus (β Car)	1.68	(S)
Alnilam (ε Ori)	1.70	
Alnair (α Gru)	1.74	(S)

List of "Naked-Eye" Variable Stars

Below is a list of 10 variable stars that can be observed with the unaided eye. All except Mira are bright enough to be observed in this way throughout their cycles; Mira at its faintest is much too faint to be seen in this way, but for part of its cycle it can easily be seen "naked-eye".

All of these stars are marked on the star maps. Locate them with certainty by using a star atlas. Then label them on the star maps just as Mira has already been labelled on Maps 1, 5, and 6. Detailed maps of the areas of the four marked by an asterisk (*) are given in the *Observer's Handbook* published by The Royal Astronomical Society of Canada. The columns headed "Max." and "Min." list the magnitude of the stars when at maximum magnitude or greatest brightness and when at minimum magnitude or least brightness. The column headed "Period" gives the length in days (unless otherwise stated) of the star's cycle or period of variability. Two of the stars have a second, much longer period, which is in addition to the shorter one. This second period may not be noticeable to the observer. The column headed "RADec#" gives the coordinates (right ascension and declination) of the star, so that it may be easily located in a star atlas. In the RADec# column, the first two numbers indicate the hour of right ascension; the second two numbers indicate the minutes of right ascension; "+" indicates its declination is north and "−" indicates it is south; the final two numbers indicate the degrees of declination.

Star	Magnitude		Period	RADec#
	Max.	Min.		
Mira (o Ceti) *	3.4	9.5	332 d.	0214-03
Rho Per	3.3	4.0	33-5, 1100	0258+38
Beta Per *	2.1	3.3	2.86731	0301+40
Lambda Tau	3.5	4.0	3.952952	0355+12
Eta Gem	3.1	3.9	233.4	0608+22
Zeta Gem	3.6	4.2	10.15073	0658+20
Alpha Her	3.0	4.0	50-130, 6yrs.	1710+14
Beta Lyrae *	3.4	4.3	12.93702	1846+33
Eta Aql	3.5	4.3	7.176641	1947+00
Delta Cep *	3.5	4.4	5.366341	2225+57

A List of the 10 Nearest "Naked Eye" Stars

The nearest star of all, of course, is our Sun. It is approximately 150,000,000 kilometres from the Earth. Light from the Sun, travelling at 300,000 kilometres per second, takes only about 8 minutes to reach the earth. We can, therefore, say that the sun is 8 light-minutes from the earth. All the other stars are much, much farther away. Their distance is measured in light years, which is the distance light travels in a year.

The list of the 50 stars nearest to our sun (published in *The Observer's Handbook* of The Royal Astronomical Society of Canada) includes many stars that are much too faint to be seen with the naked eye or with binoculars.

The list of ten stars presented here includes *only* the stars that are bright enough to be seen with the unaided eye (brighter than magnitude 6).The first number after the star indicates that star's distance in light-years from our sun. The second number indicates approximately its position on most standard lists of nearest stars. The letter "*S*" indicates that the star is in the southern part of the sky and cannot be seen from mid-northern latitudes.

The *nearest star of all to our sun* is a companion to the Alpha Centauri system called Proxima Centauri. It is much too faint to be seen with the unaided eye. Its distance is 4.22 light-years.

Star	Distance (ly)	Listed Order	
α Centauri	4.3	2	(S)
Sirius	8.6	7	
ε Eridani	10.8	10	
61 Cygni	11.1	12	
ε Indi	11.2	13	(S)
Procyon	11.4	16	
τ Ceti	11.8	20	
0² Eridani	15.7	43	
70 Ophiuchi	16.1	46	
Altair	16.5	48	

Conjunctions to Observe in 1994, 1995, and 1996

The appearance of two objects close together in the sky is called a conjunction. This is a list of the best conjuctions of bright objects visible to the naked eye during 1994, 1995 and 1996. Try to observe as many as possible. The *time* given is *approximate* local time (Daylight Time when applicable). For some events, especially involving the Moon, times vary depending on the observer's location. The *separation* of the two objects is *approximate* and in degrees. (See Chapter 4 concerning separation.) Prepare to begin observing the two objects a short while before the time given, and continue observing for a while after. Record your observations; try drawing a rough sketch to show the appearance of the objects.

Date	Time	Objects	Where to Look	Separation
1994				
Feb 3	6:00 am	Moon & Jupiter	Eastern sky	4
Apr 12	8:00 pm	Cr. Moon & Venus	Very low in western sky	1
Apr 24	9:00 pm	Moon & Spica	Moon is in eastern sky.	1
Apr 25	8:00 pm	Venus and Pleiades	Low in western sky	4
Apr 25	9:00 pm	Full Moon & Jupiter	Moon is in eastern sky.	3
Jul 10	9:00 pm	Venus & Regulus	Low in western sky	1
Jul 15	9:00 pm	Moon & Spica	Low in southwestern sky	1
Nov 30	6:00 am	Cr. Moon & Venus	Low in eastern sky	3
Mid-Dec	11:00 pm	Mars & Regulus	Eastern sky	2
1995				
Jan 14	6:00 am	Venus & Jupiter	Eastern sky	3
Jan 23	5:30 am	Moon & Spica	High in eastern sky	Note*
Jan 27	5:45 am	Cr. Moon & Venus	Low in eastern sky	1
Mar 22	5:00 am	Moon & Jupiter	High in southeastern sky	2
Apr 4	8:00 pm	Moon & Aldebaran	High in western sky	2
Apr 15	all night	Moon & Spica	Follow the Full Moon.	Note*
June 8	11:45 pm	Moon & Spica	Moon is *very* close to Spica!	
June 12	3:00 am	Full Moon & Jupiter	High in eastern sky	2
Aug 19	3:15 am	Moon & Aldebaran	High in eastern sky	2
Nov 9	5:45 am	Moon & Aldebaran	High in eastern sky	1
Dec 17	5:45 am	Moon & Spica	High in southeastern sky	2
1996				
Feb 1	7:15 pm	Venus & Saturn	Low in western sky	1
Feb 21	8:00 pm	Cr. Moon & Venus	Low in western sky	3
Apr 2	8:00 pm	Venus & Pleiades	Western sky	1
Apr 20	8:30 pm	Cr. Moon & Aldebaran	Western sky	2
Apr 28-30	8:00 pm	Mercury & Pleiades	Low in western sky	3
July 12	3:30 am	Cr. Moon & Venus	Low in northeastern sky	1
Aug 8	1:15 am	Cr. Moon & Aldebaran	Eastern sky	<1
Aug 10	3:00 am	Cr. Moon & Venus	Eastern sky	3
Sept. 2	4:30 am	Venus & Mars	Eastern sky	3
Sept. 26	9:00 pm	Full Moon & Saturn	Eastern sky	2
Oct 3 & 4	4:45 am	Venus & Regulus	Low in eastern sky	1
Nov 8	5:45 am	Cr. Moon & Venus	Low in southeastern sky	2
Dec 8	6:30 am	Cr. Moon & Venus	Low in southeastern sky	2
Dec 17	5:30 pm	Moon & Saturn	High in southern sky	3
Dec 22	all night	Full Moon & Aldebaran	Follow the Full Moon.	Note*

*During this event, the Moon *occults* or passes in front of the star. Some observers will see the star disappear and later suddenly reappear at the moon's edge. (Binoculars will help for these observations.) For the times of these events *at your location*, consult an astronomy magazine or the *Observer's Handbook*.

The Beginner's Observing Guide